113

SILVER AND GOLD

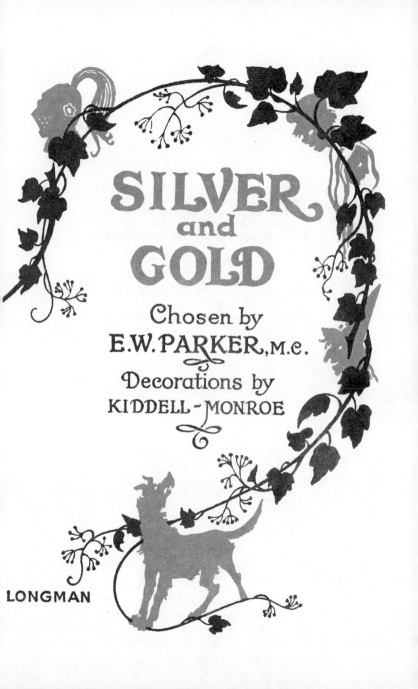

SILVER and GOLD

Chosen by
E.W. PARKER, M.C.

Decorations by
KIDDELL - MONROE

LONGMAN

LONGMAN GROUP LIMITED
London

*Associated companies, branches and representatives
throughout the world*

*First published 1957
Seventh impression 1973*

ISBN 0 582 34109 4

ENJOYING POETRY
Book 1 Silver and Gold
Book 2 For Delight
Book 3 For Your Pleasure
Book 4 A Galaxy of Poems Old and New

*Printed in Hong Kong by
Wing Tai Cheung Printing Co Ltd*

Foreword

In calling this new graded series *Enjoying Poetry* I have wished to stress its main purpose while hinting at its connection with my parallel anthology *Discovering Poetry* which owes its delightful decorations to the same artist, Mrs. Kiddell-Monroe.

In the first three books of *Enjoying Poetry*, which are based on *The Poets' Way*, there are poems written by a number of contemporary poets in an idiom familiar to modern readers, together with others that form part of our poetical heritage. All I hope will help the little books to live up to the title and encourage the reader to seek for further enjoyment from poetry, both old and new.

E.W.P.

Acknowledgments

I wish to thank my old friend Professor Gurrey for his kindness in looking at the selection at an early stage and for his valuable suggestions, and the following for permission to quote copyright material:

The author's executor for "The Pig's Tail" from *Dreamland Shores* by Norman Ault; Mrs. George Bambridge for "Puck's Song" from *Puck of Pook's Hill* by Rudyard Kipling, published by Messrs. Macmillan & Co. Ltd.; Mr. Edmund Blunden for "Quail's Nest", "Clock-A-Clay", "Autumn" and "After Reading in a Letter Proposals for Building a Cottage" by John Clare; The executors of Mary Coleridge for "The Deserted House" from *The Collected Poems of Mary Coleridge* published by Messrs. Rupert Hart-Davis Ltd.; Mr. Padraic Colum for "An Old Woman of the Roads"; Messrs. Constable & Co. Ltd. for "Kingdoms" from *Collected Poems* by O. St. John Gogarty; Mrs. H. M. Davies for "A Child's Pet" from *The Collected Poems of W. H. Davies*, published by Messrs. Jonathan Cape Ltd.; The executors of Walter de la Mare for "Ice", "The Silver Ring", "Alone", "All But Blind", "Tartary", "The Scarecrow" and "Song of Enchantment", published by Messrs. Faber & Faber Ltd.; Messrs. J. M. Dent & Sons Ltd. for "The Scout" from *A Glance Backwards* by Richard Church; The author and Messrs. J. M. Dent & Sons Ltd. for "The Adventures of Isabel" from *Family Reunion* by Ogden Nash; Mrs. Irene R. de Selincourt (Miss Irene MacLeod) for "Lone Dog"; Messrs. Gerald Duckworth & Co. Ltd. for "Lord Lundy" and "Godolphin Horne" from *Cautionary Tales* by

Hilaire Belloc; Messrs. Faber & Faber Ltd. for "The Song of the Jellicles" and "The Rum Tum Tugger" from *Old Possum's Book of Practical Cats* by T. S. Eliot; Mr. E. V. Knox for "The Spanish Main"; The author and Messrs. Macmillan & Co. Ltd. for "The River" from *Morning Songs* by Eiluned Lewis; Miss Foy Quiller-Couch for "Sage Counsel" by Sir Arthur Quiller-Couch; Dr. E. V. Rieu for "The Flattered Flying Fish" from *Cuckoo Calling*; Messrs. Sidgwick & Jackson, Ltd. and the authors' representatives for "A Ship Sails Up to Bideford" and "The Elephant" from *Poems 1912-1933* by Herbert Asquith and "Old Crow" from *The Collected Poems of John Drinkwater*; The Society of Authors, Dr. John Masefield and The Macmillan Company, New York, for "Roadways" and "West Wind" from *Collected Poems* by John Masefield, copyright 1940 by The Macmillan Company; Mrs. Stephens and Messrs. Macmillan & Co. Ltd. for "The Rivals" and "The Night" from *Collected Poems* by James Stephens; Mrs. W. B. Yeats for "The Fiddler of Dooney" and "The Song of the Old Mother" from *The Collected Poems of W. B. Yeats*, published by Messrs. Macmillan & Co. Ltd.; The Clarendon Press, Oxford, for "Robin Hood and the Butcher" and "Robin Hood and the Bishop of Hereford" from the *Oxford Book of Ballads*; and Messrs. Chatto and Windus, Ltd. for "The Horse-Trough" by Richard Hughes.

The Poems

CREATURES GREAT AND SMALL

		Page
Walter de la Mare	ALL BUT BLIND	1
Irene MacLeod	LONE DOG	2
T. S. Eliot	THE SONG OF THE JELLICLES	3
Herbert Asquith	THE ELEPHANT	4
John Drinkwater	OLD CROW	6
James Stephens	THE RIVALS	7
Norman Ault	THE PIG'S TAIL	8
Anonymous	THE THREE RAVENS	9
John Clare	QUAIL'S NEST	11
Edward FitzGerald	THE BALLAD OF JENNY THE MARE	12
John Clare	CLOCK-A-CLAY	13
T. S. Eliot	THE RUM TUM TUGGER	15
W. H. Davies	A CHILD'S PET	17

FUN AND NONSENSE

Hilaire Belloc	GODOLPHIN HORNE	18
E. V. Rieu	THE FLATTERED FLYING-FISH	20
Edward Lear	THE JUMBLIES	21
W. M. Thackeray	THE PIGTAIL	24
Hilaire Belloc	LORD LUNDY	25
Sir Arthur Quiller-Couch	SAGE COUNSEL	26
Lewis Carroll	THE LOBSTER QUADRILLE	27
Ogden Nash	ADVENTURES OF ISABEL	29
Charles Stuart Calverley	BALLAD	31
Lewis Carroll	YOU ARE OLD, FATHER WILLIAM	33
Thomas Hood	A PLAIN DIRECTION	34
Lewis Carroll	THE WALRUS AND THE CARPENTER	36
Robert Southey	THE WELL OF ST. KEYNE	40

SONGS

		Page
William Blake	REEDS OF INNOCENCE	43
Sir Walter Scott	THE OUTLAW	44
Anonymous	AN OLD FOLK SONG	47
E. Lysaght	KITTY OF COLERAINE	48
Anonymous	A CAROL	49
Anonymous	THE FINE OLD ENGLISH GENTLE-MAN	50
Sir Walter Scott	HUNTING SONG	52
William Shakespeare	OVER HILL, OVER DALE	53
Ben Jonson	WITCHES' SONG	54
Anonymous	THE MERMAID	55

PEOPLE

Sir Walter Scott	PROUD MAISIE	57
Richard Church	THE SCOUT	58
W. B. Yeats	SONG OF THE OLD MOTHER	58
Padraic Colum	AN OLD WOMAN OF THE ROADS	59
Walter de la Mare	ALONE	60
W. B. Yeats	THE FIDDLER OF DOONEY	61
John Keats	MEG MERRILIES	62
Sir Walter Scott	ALLEN-A-DALE	63
W. M. Thackeray	POCAHONTAS	65
Richard Hughes	THE HORSE TROUGH	66

THE COUNTRY LIFE

Walter de la Mare	THE SCARECROW	68
Alfred, Lord Tennyson	THE BROOK	69
Walter de la Mare	A SONG OF ENCHANTMENT	71
James Stephens	THE NIGHT	72
John Masefield	ROADWAYS	73
William Wordsworth	MARCH	74
John Clare	AUTUMN	75
Walter de la Mare	ICE	76
John Masefield	THE WEST WIND	77
James Hogg	A BOY'S SONG	79

		Page
William Blake	THE ECHOING GREEN	80
Eiluned Lewis	THE RIVER	82
John Clare	AFTER READING IN A LETTER PROPOSALS FOR BUILDING A COTTAGE	83
Mary Coleridge	THE DESERTED HOUSE	85
Anonymous	THE FAIRY QUEEN	85
Anonymous	ROBIN GOODFELLOW	88

TALES OF LONG AGO

Rudyard Kipling	PUCK'S SONG	92
Anonymous	ROBIN HOOD AND THE BISHOP OF HEREFORD	94
Anonymous	ROBIN HOOD AND THE BUTCHER	98
Robert Burns	COCK UP YOUR BEAVER	103
Matthew Arnold	SAINT BRANDAN	104
George Walter Thornbury	THE DANES	107
Robert Louis Stevenson	HEATHER ALE	108
Robert Burns	A FAREWELL	111
Frederick Marryat	THE OLD NAVY	112
Anonymous	THE SPANISH ARMADO	114

ADVENTURES

Walter de la Mare	THE SILVER PENNY	117
Herbert Asquith	A SHIP SAILS UP TO BIDEFORD	118
Edgar Allan Poe	ELDORADO	119
Walter de la Mare	TARTARY	120
Anonymous	THERE WAS A KNIGHT	121
James Russell Lowell	SINGING LEAVES	123
Anonymous	THE WEE WEE MAN	128
Charles Kingsley	EARL HALDAN'S DAUGHTER	130
E. V. Knox	THE SPANISH MAIN	131
Anonymous	THE WRAGGLE TAGGLE GIPSIES	132
Robert Browning	BOOT AND SADDLE	134
Oliver St. John Gogarty	KINGDOMS	135

		Page
Robert Browning	HERVÉ RIEL	136
R. H. Barham (Thomas Ingoldsby)	THE JACKDAW OF RHEIMS	143
Anonymous	GREEN BROOM	149
Matthew Arnold	THE NECKAN	150
Anonymous	THE GIPSY LADDIE	153
Robert Browning	THE PIED PIPER OF HAMELIN	155
Thomas Campbell	LORD ULLIN'S DAUGHTER	166
Matthew Arnold	THE FORSAKEN MERMAN	169

The Poets

	Page
Arnold, Matthew (1822–1888)	104, 150, 169
Asquith, Herbert (1881–1947)	4, 118
Ault, Norman (1880–1950)	8
Barham, R. H. (1788–1845)	143
Belloc, Hilaire (1870–1953)	18, 25
Blake, William (1757–1827)	43, 80
Browning, Robert (1812–1889)	134, 136, 155
Burns, Robert (1759–1796)	103, 111
Calverley, Charles Stuart (1831–1884)	31
Campbell, Thomas (1777–1844)	166
Carroll, Lewis (1832–1898)	27, 33, 36
Church, Richard (born 1893)	58
Clare, John (1793–1864)	11, 13, 75, 83
Coleridge, Mary (1861–1907)	85
Colum, Padraic (born 1881)	59
Davies, W. H. (1871–1940)	17
De la Mare, Walter (1873–1956)	1, 60, 68, 71, 76, 117, 120
Drinkwater, John (1882–1937)	6
Eliot, T. S. (born 1888)	3, 15
FitzGerald, Edward (1809–1883)	12
Gogarty, Oliver St. John (1878–1957)	135
Hogg, James (1770–1835)	79
Hood, Thomas (1799–1845)	34
Hughes, Richard (born 1900)	66
Jonson, Ben (1573–1637)	54
Keats, John (1795–1821)	62
Kingsley, Charles (1819–1875)	130
Kipling, Rudyard (1865–1936)	92

	Page
Knox, E. V. (born 1881)	131
Lear, Edward (1812–1888)	21
Lewis, Eiluned	82
Lowell, James Russell (1819–1891)	123
Lysaght, Edward (1763–1811)	48
McLeod, Irene (born 1891)	2
Marryat, Frederick (1792–1848)	112
Masefield, John (born 1878)	73, 77
Nash, Ogden (born 1902)	29
Poe, Edgar Allan (1809–1849)	119
Quiller-Couch, Sir Arthur (1863–1944)	26
Rieu, E. V. (born 1887)	20
Scott, Sir Walter (1771–1832)	44, 52, 57, 63
Shakespeare, William (1564–1616)	53
Southey, Robert (1774–1843)	40
Stephens, James (1882–1950)	7, 72
Stevenson, Robert Louis (1850–1894)	108
Tennyson, Alfred Lord (1809–1892)	69
Thackeray, William Makepeace (1811–1863)	24, 65
Thornbury, George Walter (1828–1876)	107
Wordsworth, William (1770–1850)	74
Yeats, W. B. (1865–1939)	58, 61

CREATURES GREAT AND SMALL

All But Blind

ALL but blind
    In his chambered hole
Groves for worms
    The four-clawed Mole.

All but blind
    In the evening sky,
The hooded Bat
    Twirls softly by.

All but blind
    In the burning day
The Barn-Owl blunders
    On her way.

And blind as are
    These three to me,
So, blind to Someone
    I must be.

WALTER DE LA MARE

Lone Dog

I'M a lean dog, a keen dog, a wild dog, and lone;
  I'm a rough dog, a tough dog, hunting on my
                            own;
I'm a bad dog, a mad dog, teasing silly sheep;
I love to sit and bay the moon, to keep fat souls
                           from sleep.

I'll never be a lap dog, licking dirty feet,
A sleek dog, a meek dog, cringing for my meat;
Not for me the fireside, the well-filled plate,
But shut door, and sharp stone, and cuff, and kick,
                           and hate.

Not for me the other dogs, running by my side;
Some have run a short while, but none of them
                           would bide.
O mine is still the lone trail, the hard trail, the
                           best,
Wide wind, and wild stars, and the hunger of the
                           quest!

IRENE MCLEOD

2

The Song of the Jellicles

Jellicle Cats come out to-night,
   Jellicle Cats come one come all:
The Jellicle Moon is shining bright—
Jellicles come to the Jellicle Ball.

Jellicle Cats are black and white,
Jellicle Cats are rather small;
Jellicle Cats are merry and bright,
And pleasant to hear when they caterwaul,
Jellicle Cats have cheerful faces,
Jellicle Cats have bright black eyes;
They like to practise their airs and graces
And wait for the Jellicle Moon to rise.

Jellicle Cats develop slowly,
Jellicle Cats are not too big;
Jellicle Cats are roly-poly,
They know how to dance a gavotte and a jig.
Until the Jellicle Moon appears
They make their toilette and take their repose:
Jellicles wash behind their ears
Jellicles dry between their toes.

Jellicle Cats are white and black,
Jellicle Cats are of moderate size;
Jellicles jump like a jumping-jack,
Jellicle Cats have moonlit eyes.
They're quiet enough in the morning hours,
They're quiet enough in the afternoon,
Reserving their terpsichorean[1] powers
To dance by the light of the Jellicle Moon.

Jellicle Cats are black and white,
Jellicle Cats (as I said) are small;
If it happens to be a stormy night
They will practise a caper or two in the hall.
If it happens the sun is shining bright
You would say they had nothing to do at all:
They are resting and saving themselves to be right
For the Jellicle Moon and the Jellicle Ball.

T. S. ELIOT

The Elephant

HERE comes the elephant
        Swaying along
With his cargo of children
All singing a song:
To the tinkle of laughter
He goes on his way,
And his cargo of children
Have crowned him with may.

[1] terpsichorean: of the nature of dancing.

His legs are in leather
And padded his toes;
He can root up an oak
With a whisk of his nose;
With a wave of his trunk
And a turn of his chin
He can pull down a house,
Or pick up a pin.
Beneath his grey forehead
A little eye peers;
Of what is he thinking
Between those wide ears?

What does he feel?
If he wished to tease,
He could twirl his keeper
Over the trees;
If he were not kind,
He could play cup and ball
With Robert and Helen
And Uncle Paul;

But that grey forehead,
Those crinkled ears
Have learned to be kind
In a hundred years:
And so with the children
He goes on his way
To the tinkle of laughter
And crowned with the may.

HERBERT ASQUITH

Old Crow

THE bird in the corn
    Is a marvellous crow,
He was laid and was born
    In the season of snow;
And he chants his old catches
Like a ghost under hatches.

He comes from the shades
    Of his wood very early,
And works in the blades
    Of the wheat and the barley,
And he's happy, although
He's a grumbleton crow.

The larks have devices
    For sunny delight,
And the sheep in their fleeces
    Are woolly and white;
But these things are the scorn
Of the bird in the corn.

And morning goes by
    And still he is there,
Till a rose in the sky
    Calls him back to his lair
In the boughs, where the gloom
Is a part of his plume.

6

But the boy in the lane
    With his gun, by and by,
To the heart of the grain
    Will narrowly spy,
And the twilight will come,
And no crow will fly home.

JOHN DRINKWATER

The Rivals

I HEARD a bird at dawn
    Singing sweetly on a tree,
That the dew was on the lawn,
And the wind was on the lea;
But I didn't listen to him,
For he didn't sing to me!

I didn't listen to him,
For he didn't sing to me
That the dew was on the lawn,
And the wind was on the lea!
I was singing at the time
Just as prettily as he!

I was singing all the time,
Just as prettily as he,
About the dew upon the lawn,
And the wind upon the lea!
So I didn't listen to him,
As he sang upon a tree!

JAMES STEPHENS

The Pig's Tail

A FURRY coat has the bear to wear,
    The tortoise a coat of mail,
The yak has more than his share of hair,
    But—the pig has the curly tail.

The elephant's tusks are sold for gold,
    The slug leaves a silver trail,
The parrot is never too old to scold,
    But—the pig has the curly tail.

The lion can either roar or snore,
    The cow gives milk in a pail,
The dog can guard a door, and more,
    But—the pig has the curly tail.

The monkey makes you smile a while,
    The tiger makes you quail,
The fox has many a wile of guile,
    But—the pig has the curly tail.

For the rest of the beasts that prey or play,
   From tiny mouse to the whale,
There's much that I could say to-day,
   But—the pig has the curly tail.

NORMAN AULT

The Three Ravens

THERE were three ravens sat on a tree,
   Downe a downe, hay downe, hay downe,
There were three ravens sat on a tree,
              With a downe—
There were three ravens sat on a tree,
They were as black as they might be.
   With a down derrie, derrie, derrie, downe,
                downe.

The one of them said to his mate,
"Where shall we our breakfast take?"

"Downe in yonder greenè field,
There lies a knight slaine under his shield.

"His hounds they lie down at his feete,
So well they can their master keepe.

"His haukes they fly so eagerly,
There's no fowl dare come him nie."

Downe there comes a fallow doe,
As great with yonge as she might goe.

She lift up his bloudy head,
And kist his wounds that were so red.

She got him up upon her backe,
And carried him to earthen lake.

She buried him before the prime,
She was dead herself ere even-song time.

God send every gentleman,
Such haukes, such hounds, and such a lemàn![1]

ANONYMOUS

[1] leman: sweetheart.

Quail's Nest

I WANDERED out one rainy day
　　And heard a bird with merry joys
Cry "wet my foot" for half the way;
　　I stood and wondered at the noise,

When from my foot a bird did flee—
　　The rain flew bouncing from her breast—
I wondered what the bird could be,
　　And almost trampled on her nest.

The nest was full of eggs and round—
　　I met a shepherd in the vales,
And stood to tell him what I found.
　　He knew and said it was a quail's,

For he himself the nest had found,
　　Among the wheat and on the green,
When going on his daily round,
　　With eggs as many as fifteen.

Among the stranger birds they feed,
　　Their summer flight is short and low;
There's very few know where they breed,
　　And scarcely any where they go.

JOHN CLARE

The Ballad of Jenny the Mare

I'LL sing you a song, and a merry merry song,
 Concerning our Yorkshire Jen;
Who ne'er yet ran with horse or mare,
 That ever she cared for a pin.

When first she came to Newmarket town,
 The sportsmen all viewed her around;
All the cry was, "Alas, poor wench,
 Thou never can run this ground!"

When they came to the starting-post,
 The Mare looked very smart;
And let them all say what they will,
 She never lost her start.

When they got to the two-mile post,
 Poor Jenny was cast behind:
She was cast behind, she was cast behind,
 All for to take her wind.

When they got to the three-mile post,
 The Mare look'd very pale—
SHE LAID DOWN HER EARS ON HER BONNY NECK,
 AND BY THEM ALL DID SHE SAIL.

"Come follow me, come follow me,
    All you that run so neat;
And ere that you catch me again
    I'll make you all to sweat."

When she got to the winning-post,
    The people all gave a shout;
And Jenny click'd up her lily-white foot,
    And jumped like any buck.

The Jockey said to her, "This race you have run,
    This race for me you have got;
You could gallop it all over again,
    When the rest could hardly trot!"

EDWARD FITZGERALD

Clock-a-Clay[1]

IN the cowslip pips I lie,
    Hidden from the buzzing fly,
While green grass beneath me lies,
Pearled with dew like fishes' eyes,
Here I lie, a clock-a-clay,
Waiting for the time of day.

[1] Clock-a-clay: ladybird.

13

While grassy forest quakes surprise,
And the wild wind sobs and sighs,
My gold home rocks as like to.fall,
On its pillar green and tall;
When the pattering rain drives by
Clock-a-clay keeps warm and dry.

Day by day and night by night,
All the week I hide from sight;
In the cowslip pips I lie,
In rain and dew still warm and dry;
Day and night, and night and day
Red, black-spotted clock-a-clay.

My home shakes in wind and showers,
Pale green pillar topped with flowers,
Bending at the wild wind's breath,
Till I touch the grass beneath;
Here I live, lone clock-a-clay,
Watching for the time of day.

JOHN CLARE

The Rum Tum Tugger

THE Rum Tum Tugger is a Curious Cat:
    If you offer him pheasant he would rather
                    have grouse.
If you put him in a house he would much prefer
                    a flat,
If you put him in a flat then he'd rather have a
                    house.
If you set him on a mouse then he only wants a rat,
If you set him on a rat then he'd rather chase a
                    mouse.
Yes the Rum Tum Tugger is a Curious Cat—
    And there isn't any call for me to shout it:
        For he will do
        As he do do
            And there's no doing anything
                    about it!

The Rum Tum Tugger is a terrible bore:
When you let him in, then he wants to be out;
He's always on the wrong side of every door,
And as soon as he's at home, then he'd like to get
                    about.
He likes to lie in the bureau drawer,
But he makes such a fuss if he can't get out.
Yes the Rum Tum Tugger is a Curious Cat—
    And it isn't any use for you to doubt it:
        For he will do
        As he do do
            And there's no doing anything
                    about it!

The Rum Tum Tugger is a curious beast:
His disobliging ways are a matter of habit.
If you offer him fish then he always wants a feast;
When there isn't any fish then he won't eat rabbit.
If you offer him cream then he sniffs and sneers,
For he only likes what he finds for himself;
So you'll catch him in it right up to the ears,
If you put it away on the larder shelf. ·
The Rum Tum Tugger is artful and knowing,
The Rum Tum Tugger doesn't care for a cuddle;
But he'll leap on your lap in the middle of your
sewing,
For there's nothing he enjoys like a horrible
muddle.
Yes the Rum Tum Tugger is a Curious Cat—
And there isn't any need for me to spout it:
For he will do
As he do do
And there's no doing anything
about it!

T. S. ELIOT

A Child's Pet

WHEN I sailed out of Baltimore
     With twice a thousand head of sheep,
They would not eat, they would not drink,
   But bleated o'er the deep.

Inside the pens we crawled each day,
   To sort the living from the dead;
And when we reached the Mersey's mouth
   Had lost five hundred head.

Yet every night and day one sheep,
   That had no fear of man or sea,
Stuck through the bars its pleading face,
   And it was stroked by me.

And to the sheep-men standing near,
   "You see," I said, "this one tame sheep:
It seems a child has lost her pet,
   And cried herself to sleep."

So every time we passed it by,
   Sailing to England's slaughter-house,
Eight ragged sheep-men—tramps and thieves—
Would stroke that sheep's black nose.

                              W. H. DAVIES

FUN AND NONSENSE

Godolphin Horne

*Who was cursed with the Sin of Pride, and
Became a Boot-Black*

GODOLPHIN HORNE was nobly born;
He held the human race in scorn,
And lived with all his sisters where
His father lived, in Berkeley Square.
And oh! the lad was deathly proud!
He never shook your hand or bowed,
But merely smirked and nodded thus:
How perfectly ridiculous!
Alas! That such affected tricks
Should flourish in a child of six!
(For such was young Godolphin's age.)
Just then, the Court required a page,
Whereat the Lord High Chamberlain
(The kindest and the best of men),
He went good-naturedly and took
A perfectly enormous book
Called *People Qualified to Be
Attendant on His Majesty*.
And murmured, as he scanned the list
(To see that no one should be missed),
"There's William Coutts has got the 'flu,

And Billy Higgs would never do,
And Guy de Vere is far too young.
And . . . wasn't D'Alton's father hung?
And as for Alexander Byng! . . .
I think I know the kind of thing,
A churchman, cleanly, nobly born,
Come let us say Godolphin Horne?
But hardly had he said the word
When murmurs of dissent were heard.
The King of Iceland's eldest son
Said, "Thank you! I am taking none!"
The aged Duchess of Athlone
Remarked, in her sub-acid tone,
"I doubt if he is what we need!"
With which the bishops all agreed;
And even Lady Mary Flood
(*So* kind, and oh! so *really* good)
Said, "No! He wouldn't do at all,
He'd make us feel a lot too small."
The Chamberlain said, ". . . Well, well, well!
No doubt you're right. . . . One cannot tell!"
He took his gold and diamond pen
And scratched Godolphin out again.
So now Godolphin is the boy
Who blacks the boots at the Savoy.

HILAIRE BELLOC

The Flattered Flying-fish

SAID the Shark to the Flying-Fish over the phone:
"Will you join me to-night? I am dining
                                          alone.

Let me order a nice little dinner for two!
And come as you are, in your shimmering blue."

Said the Flying-Fish: "Fancy remembering me,
And the dress that I wore at the Porpoises' tea!"
"How could I forget?" said the Shark in his guile:
"I expect you at eight!" and rang off with a smile.

She has powdered her nose; she has put on her
                                              things;
She is off with one flap of her luminous wings.
O little one, lovely, light-hearted and vain,
The moon will not shine on your beauty again!

E. V. RIEU

The Jumblies

THEY went to sea in a Sieve, they did,
   In a Sieve they went to sea:
In spite of all their friends could say,
On a winter's morn, on a stormy day,
   In a Sieve they went to sea!
And when the Sieve turned round and round,
And every one cried, "You'll all be drowned!"
They called aloud, "Our Sieve ain't big,
But we don't care a button! we don't care a fig!
   In a Sieve we'll go to sea!"
      Far and few, far and few,
         Are the lands where the Jumblies live;
         Their heads are green, and their hands are blue,
            And they went to sea in a Sieve.

They sailed away in a Sieve, they did,
   In a Sieve they sailed so fast,
With only a beautiful pea-green veil
Tied with a riband by way of a sail,
   To a small tobacco-pipe mast;
And every one said, who saw them go,
"O won't they be soon upset, you know!
For the sky is dark, and the voyage is long,
And happen what may, it's extremely wrong
   In a Sieve to sail so fast!"
      Far and few, far and few,
         Are the lands where the Jumblies live;
         Their heads are green, and their hands are blue,
            And they went to sea in a Sieve.

The water it soon came in, it did,
    The water it soon came in;
So to keep them dry, they wrapped their feet
In a pinky paper all folded neat,
    And they fastened it down with a pin.
And they passed the night in a crockery-jar,
And each of them said, "How wise we are!
Though the sky be dark, and the voyage be long,
Yet we never can think we were rash or wrong,
    While round in our Sieve we spin!"
      Far and few, far and few,
        Are the lands where the Jumblies live;
        Their heads are green, and their hands are blue,
        And they went to sea in a Sieve.

And all night long they sailed away;
    And when the sun went down,
They whistled and warbled a moony song
To the echoing sound of a coppery gong,
    In the shade of the mountains brown.
"O Timballo! How happy we are,
When we live in a sieve and a crockery-jar,
And all night long in the moonlight pale,
We sail away with a pea-green sail,
    In the shade of the mountains brown!"
      Far and few, far and few,
        Are the lands where the Jumblies live;
        Their heads are green, and their hands are blue,
        And they went to sea in a Sieve.

They sailed to the Western Sea, they did,
    To a land all covered with trees,
And they bought an Owl, and a useful Cart,
And a pound of Rice and a Cranberry Tart,
    And a hive of silvery Bees.
And they bought a Pig, and some green Jackdaws,
And a lovely Monkey with lollipop paws,
And forty bottles of Ring-Bo-Ree,
    And no end of Stilton Cheese.
      Far and few, far and few,
        Are the lands where the Jumblies live;
      Their heads are green and their hands are blue,
        And they went to sea in a Sieve.

And in twenty years they all came back,
    In twenty years or more,
And everyone said, "How tall they've grown!
For they've been to the Lakes, and the Terrible
    And the hills of the Chankly Bore";   [Zone,
And they drank their health, and gave them a feast
Of dumplings made of beautiful yeast;
And everyone said, "If we only live,
We too will go to sea in a Sieve,—
    To the hills of the Chankly Bore!"
      Far and few, far and few,
        Are the lands where the Jumblies live;
      Their heads are green, and their hands are blue,
        And they went to sea in a Sieve.

EDWARD LEAR

The Pigtail

THERE lived a sage in days of yore,
   And he a handsome pigtail wore:
But wondered much and sorrowed more
   Because it hung behind him.

He mused upon this curious case,
And swore he'd change the pigtail's place,
And have it hanging at his face,
   Not dangling there behind him.

Says he, "The mystery I've found—
I'll turn me round"—he turned him round;
   But still it hung behind him.

Then round, and round, and out and in,
All day the puzzled sage did spin;
In vain—it mattered not a pin—
   The pigtail hung behind him.

And right, and left, and round about,
And up and down, and in and out,
He turned; but still the pigtail stout
   Hung steadily behind him.

And though his efforts never slack,
And though he twist, and twirl, and tack,
Alas! still faithful to his back
   The pigtail hangs behind him.

W. M. THACKERAY

Lord Lundy

LORD LUNDY from his earliest years
　　Was far too freely moved to Tears.
For instance, if his Mother said,
"Lundy! It's time to go to Bed!"
He bellowed like a Little Turk.
Or if his father, Lord Dunquerque
Said, "Hi!" in a Commanding Tone,
"Hi, Lundy! Leave the Cat alone!"
Lord Lundy, letting go its tail,
Would raise so terrible a wail
As moved
His Grandpapa the Duke
To utter the severe rebuke:
"When I, Sir! was a little Boy,
An Animal was not a Toy!"
His father's Elder Sister, who
Was married to a Parvenoo,
Confided to Her Husband, "Drat!
The Miserable, Peevish Brat!
Why don't they drown the Little Beast?"
Suggestions which, to say the least,
Are not what we expect to hear
From Daughters of an English Peer.
His grandmamma, His Mother's Mother,
Who had some dignity or other,
The Garter, or no matter what,
I can't remember all the Lot!
Said, "Oh! that I were Brisk and Spry
To give him that for which to cry!"
(An empty wish, alas! for she

Was Blind and nearly ninety-three.)
The Dear Old Butler thought—but there!
I really neither know nor care
For what the Dear Old Butler thought!
In my opinion, Butlers ought
To know their place, and not to play
The Old Retainer night and day.
I'm getting tired and so are you,
Let's cut the Poem into two!

HILAIRE BELLOC

Sage Counsel

THE lion is the beast to fight:
   He leaps along the plain,
And if you run with all your might,
  He runs with all his mane.
    I'm glad I'm not a Hottentot,
    But if I were, with outward callum
    I'd either faint upon the spot
    Or hie me up a leafy pallum.

The chamois is the beast to hunt:
  He's fleeter than the wind,
And when the chamois is in front
  The hunter is behind.
    The Tyrolese make famous cheese
    And hunt the chamois o'er the chazzums;
    I'll choose the former, if you please,
    For precipices give me spazzums.

26

The polar bear will make a rug
    Almost as white as snow:
But if he gets you in his hug,
    He rarely lets you go.
        And Polar ice looks very nice,
        With all the colours of a prizzum;
        But, if you'll follow my advice,
        Stay home and learn your catechizzum.

SIR ARTHUR QUILLER-COUCH

The Lobster Quadrille

"WILL you walk a little faster?" said a whiting
                   to a snail,
"There's a porpoise close behind us, and he's
               treading on my tail.
See how eagerly the lobsters and the turtles all
                   advance!
They are waiting on the shingle—will you come
              and join the dance?
Will you, won't you, will you, won't you, will you
               join the dance?
Will you, won't you, will you, won't you, won't
            you join the dance?

27

"You can really have no notion how delightful it
will be,
When they take us up and throw us, with the
lobsters, out to sea!"
But the snail replied, "Too far, too far!" and
gave a look askance—
Said he thanked the whiting kindly, but he would
not join the dance.
Would not, could not, would not, could not,
would not join the dance.
Would not, could not, would not, could not, could
not join the dance.

"What matters it how far we go?" his scaly friend
replied.
"There is another shore, you know, upon the
other side.
The further off from England the nearer is to
France—
Then turn not pale, belovèd snail, but come and
join the dance.
Will you, won't you, will you, won't you, will
you join the dance?
Will you, won't you, will you, won't you, won't
you join the dance?"

LEWIS CARROLL

Adventures of Isabel

ISABEL met an enormous bear,
  Isabel, Isabel, didn't care;
The bear was hungry, the bear was ravenous,
The bear's big mouth was cruel and cavernous.
The bear said, Isabel, glad to meet you.
How do, Isabel, now I'll eat you!
Isabel, Isabel, didn't worry,
Isabel didn't scream or scurry.
She washed her hands and she
                    straightened her hair up,
Then Isabel quietly ate the bear up.

Once in a night as black as pitch
Isabel met a wicked old witch.
The witch's face was cross and wrinkled,
The witch's gums with teeth were sprinkled.
Ho, ho, Isabel! the old witch crowed,
I'll turn you into an ugly toad!
Isabel, Isabel, didn't worry,
Isabel didn't scream or scurry,
She showed no rage and she showed no rancour,
But she turned the witch into milk and drank her.

29

Isabel met a hideous giant,
Isabel continued self-reliant.
The giant was hairy, the giant was horrid,
He had one eye in the middle of his forehead.
Good morning Isabel, the giant said,
I'll grind your bones to make my bread.
Isabel, Isabel, didn't worry,
Isabel didn't scream or scurry.
She nibbled the zwieback that she always fed off,
And when it was gone, she cut the giant's head off.

Isabel met a troublesome doctor,
He punched and he poked till he really shocked her.
The doctor's talk was of coughs and chills
And the doctor's satchel bulged with pills.
The doctor said unto Isabel,
Swallow this, it will make you well.
Isabel, Isabel, didn't worry,
Isabel didn't scream or scurry.
She took those pills from the pill concocter,
And Isabel calmly cured the doctor.

OGDEN NASH

30

Ballad

PART I

THE auld wife sat at her ivied door,
   (*Butter and eggs and a pound of cheese*)
A thing she had frequently done before,
   And her spectacles lay on her apron'd knees.

The piper he piped on the hill-top high,
   (*Butter and eggs and a pound of cheese*)
Till the cow said, "I die," and the goose ask'd,
                                             "Why?"
   And the dog said nothing, but search'd for fleas.

The farmer he strode through the square
                                       farmyard;
   (*Butter and eggs and a pound of cheese*)
His last brew of ale was a trifle hard—
   The connexion of which with the plot one sees.

The farmer's daughter hath frank blue eyes;
   (*Butter and eggs and a pound of cheese*)
She hears the rooks caw in the windy skies,
   As she sits in her lattice and shells her peas.

The farmer's daughter hath ripe red lips;
   (*Butter and eggs and a pound of cheese*)
If you try to approach her, away she skips
   Over tables and chairs with apparent ease.

The farmer's daughter hath soft brown hair;
   (*Butter and eggs and a pound of cheese*)
And I met with a ballad, I can't say where,
   Which wholly consisted of lines like these.

PART II

She sat with her hands 'neath her dimpled cheeks,
   (*Butter and eggs and a pound of cheese*)
And spake not a word. While a lady speaks
   There is hope, but she didn't even sneeze.

She sat with her hands 'neath her crimson cheeks;
   (*Butter and eggs and a pound of cheese*)
She gave up mending her father's breeks,
   And let the cat roll in her new chemise.

She sat with her hands 'neath her burning cheeks,
   (*Butter and eggs and a pound of cheese*)
And gazed at the piper for thirteen weeks;
   Then she follow'd him out o'er the misty leas.

Her sheep follow'd her, as their tails did them.
   (*Butter and eggs and a pound of cheese*)
And this song is consider'd a perfect gem,
   And as to the meaning, it's what you please.

CHARLES STUART CALVERLEY

You Are Old, Father William

"You are old, Father William", the young man
                                    said,
   "And your hair has become very white;
And yet you incessantly stand on your head—
   Do you think, at your age, it is right?"

"In my youth," Father William replied to his son,
   "I feared it might injure the brain;
But now that I'm perfectly sure I have none,
   Why, I do it again and again."

"You are old," said the youth, "as I mentioned
                                    before,
   And have grown most uncommonly fat;
Yet you turned a back-somersault in at the door—
   Pray, what is the reason of that?"

"In my youth," said the sage, as he shook his
                                    grey locks,
   "I kept all my limbs very supple
By the use of this ointment—one shilling the box—
   Allow me to sell you a couple."

"You are old," said the youth, "and your jaws
                                    are too weak
   For anything tougher than suet;
Yet you finished the goose, with the bones and
                                    the beak—
   Pray, how did you manage to do it?"

33

"In my youth," said his father, "I took to the law,
    And argued each case with my wife;
And the muscular strength which it gave to my jaw
    Has lasted the rest of my life."

"You are old," said the youth; "one would
                                    hardly suppose
    That your eye was as steady as ever;
Yet you balanced an eel on the end of your nose—
    What made you so awfully clever?"

"I have answered three questions, and that is
                                    enough,"
    Said his father; "don't give yourself airs!
Do you think I can listen all day to such stuff?
    Be off, or I'll kick you down stairs!"

LEWIS CARROLL

A Plain Direction

IN London once I lost my way
    In faring to and fro,
And asked a little ragged boy
    The way that I should go;
He gave a nod, and then a wink,
    And told me to get there
"Straight down the Crooked Lane,
    And all round the Square."

34

I boxed his little saucy ears,
   And then away I strode;
But since, I've found that weary path
   Is quite a common road.
Utopia is a pleasant place,
   But how shall I get there?
"Straight down the Crooked Lane,
   And all round the Square."

I've read about a famous town
   That drove a famous trade,
Where Whittington walked up and found
   A fortune ready made.
The very streets are paved with gold;
   But how shall I get there?
"Straight down the Crooked Lane,
   And all round the Square."

I've read about a Fairy Land,
   In some romantic tale,
Where Dwarfs, if good, are sure to thrive,
   And wicked Giants fail.
My wish is great, my shoes are strong,
   But how shall I get there?
"Straight down the Crooked Lane,
   And all round the Square."

I've heard about a pleasant land,
    Where omelettes grow on trees,
And roasted pigs run, crying out,
    "Come eat me, if you please."
My appetite is rather keen,
    But how shall I get there?
"Straight down the Crooked Lane,
    And all rŏund the Square."

THOMAS HOOD

The Walrus and the Carpenter

THE sun was shining on the sea,
    Shining with all his might:
He did his very best to make
The billows smooth and bright—
And this was odd, because it was
The middle of the night.

The moon was shining sulkily,
Because she thought the sun
Had got no business to be there
After the day was done—
"It's very rude of him," she said,
"To come and spoil the fun."

The sea was wet as wet could be,
The sands were dry as dry.
You could not see a cloud, because

36

No cloud was in the sky:
No birds were flying overhead—
There were no birds to fly.

The Walrus and the Carpenter
Were walking close at hand;
They wept like anything to see
Such quantities of sand:
"If this were only cleared away,"
They said, "it *would* be grand!"

"If seven maids with seven mops
Swept it for half a year,
Do you suppose," the Walrus said,
"That they could get it clear?"
"I doubt it," said the Carpenter,
And shed a bitter tear.

"O Oysters, come and walk with us!"
The Walrus did beseech.
"A pleasant walk, a pleasant talk,
Along the briny beach:
We cannot do with more than four,
To give a hand to each."

The eldest Oyster looked at him,
But never a word he said:
The eldest Oyster winked his eye,
And shook his heavy head—
Meaning to say he did not choose
To leave the oyster-bed.

But four young Oysters hurried up,
All eager for the treat:
Their coats were brushed, their faces washed,
Their shoes were clean and neat—
And this was odd, because, you know,
They hadn't any feet.

Four other Oysters followed them,
And yet another four;
And thick and fast they came at last,
And more, and more, and more—
All hopping through the frothy waves,
And scrambling to the shore.

The Walrus and the Carpenter
Walked on a mile or so,
And then they rested on a rock
Conveniently low:
And all the little Oysters stood
And waited in a row.

"The time has come," the Walrus said,
"To talk of many things:
Of shoes—and ships—and sealing-wax—
Of cabbages—and kings—
And why the sea is boiling hot—
And whether pigs have wings."

"But, wait a bit," the Oysters cried,
"Before we have our chat;
For some of us are out of breath,
And all of us are fat!"
"No hurry!" said the Carpenter.
They thanked him much for that.

"A loaf of bread," the Walrus said,
"Is what we chiefly need:
Pepper and vinegar besides
Are very good indeed—
Now if you're ready, Oysters dear,
We can begin to feed."

"But not on us!" the Oysters cried,
Turning a little blue.
"After such kindness, that would be
A dismal thing to do!"
"The night is fine," the Walrus said,
"Do you admire the view?

"It was so kind of you to come:
And you are very nice!"
The Carpenter said nothing but,
"Cut us another slice:
I wish you were not quite so deaf—
I've had to ask you twice!"

"It seems a shame," the Walrus said,
"To play them such a trick,
After we've brought them out so far,
And made them trot so quick!"
The Carpenter said nothing but,
"The butter's spread too thick."

"I weep for you," the Walrus said,
"I deeply sympathize."
With sobs and tears he sorted out
Those of the largest size,
Holding his pocket-handkerchief
Before his streaming eyes.

"O Oysters," said the Carpenter,
"You've had a pleasant run!
Shall we be trotting home again?"
But answer there was none—
And this was scarcely odd, because
They'd eaten every one.

LEWIS CARROLL

The Well of St. Keyne

A WELL there is in the west country,
And a clearer one never was seen;
There is not a wife in the west country
But has heard of the Well of St. Keyne.

An oak and an elm-tree stand beside,
   And behind doth an ash-tree grow,
And a willow from the bank above
   Droops to the water below.

A traveller came to the Well of St. Keyne.
   Joyfully he drew nigh,
For from cock-crow he had been travelling,
   And there was not a cloud in the sky.

He drank of the water so cool and clear,
   For thirsty and hot was he,
And he sat down upon the bank
   Under the willow-tree.

There came a man from the house hard by
   At the Well to fill his pail;
On the Well-side he rested it,
   And he bade the stranger hail.

"Now art thou a bachelor, stranger?" quoth he,
   "For an if thou hast a wife,
The happiest draught thou hast drunk this day
   That ever thou didst in thy life.

"Or hast thy good woman, if one thou hast,
   Ever here in Cornwall been?
For an if she have, I'll venture my life
   She has drunk of the Well of St. Keyne."

"I have left a good woman who never was here,"
    The stranger he made reply,
"But that my draught should be the better for that,
    I pray you answer me why."

"St. Keyne," quoth the Cornish-man, "many a time
    Drank of this crystal Well,
And before the Angel summoned her,
    She laid on the water a spell.

"If the husband of this gifted Well
    Shall drink before his wife,
A happy man thenceforth is he,
    For he shall be master for life.

"But if the wife should drink of it first—
    God help the husband then!"
The stranger stooped to the Well of St. Keyne,
    And drank of the water again.

"You drank of the Well I warrant betimes?"
    He to the Cornish-man said:
But the Cornish-man smiled as the stranger spake,
    And sheepishly shook his head.

"I hastened as soon as the wedding was done,
    And left my wife in the porch;
But i' faith she had been wiser than me,
    For she took a bottle to church."

ROBERT SOUTHEY

SONGS

Reeds of Innocence

PIPING down the valleys wild,
    Piping songs of pleasant glee,
On a cloud I saw a child,
    And he laughing said to me:

"Pipe a song about a Lamb!"
    So I piped with merry cheer.
"Piper, pipe that song again";
    So I piped: he wept to hear.

"Drop thy pipe, thy happy pipe;
    Sing thy songs of happy cheer";
So I sang the same again,
    While he wept with joy to hear.

"Piper, sit thee down and write
    In a book, that all may read."
So he vanished from my sight,
    And I pluck'd a hollow reed,

And I made a rural pen,
    And I stained the water clear,
And I wrote my happy songs
    Every child may joy to hear.

WILLIAM BLAKE

43

The Outlaw

O, BRIGNAL banks are wild and fair,
   And Greta woods are green,
And you may gather garlands there
   Would grace a summer queen.
And as I rode by Dalton Hall
   Beneath the turrets high,
A maiden on the castle wall
   Was singing merrily:—

Chorus

"O, Brignal banks are fresh and fair,
   And Greta woods are green;
I'd rather rove with Edmund there,
   Than reign our English queen."

—"If, maiden, thou wouldst wend with me.
   To leave both tower and town,
Thou first must guess what life lead we
   That dwell by dale and down.
And if thou canst that riddle read,
   As read full well you may,
Then to the greenwood shalt thou speed
   As blithe as Queen of May."

Yet sung she, "Brignal banks are fair,
    And Greta woods are green;
I'd rather rove with Edmund there,
    Than reign our English queen

"I read you, by your bugle-horn
    And by your palfrey good,
I read you for a ranger sworn
    To keep the king's greenwood."
—"A ranger, lady, winds his horn,
    And 'tis at peep of light;
His blast is heard at merry morn,
    And mine at dead of night."

Chorus
Yet sung she, "Brignal banks are fair,
    And Greta woods are gay;
I would I were with Edmund there
    To reign his Queen of May!

"With burnish'd brand[1] and musketoon[2]
    So gallantly you come.
I read you for a bold dragoon
    That lists the tuck of drum."
—"I list no more the tuck of drum,
    No more the trumpet hear;
But when the beetle sounds his hum,
    My comrades take the spear.

[1] A sword.   [2] A short musket.

"And oh! though Brignal banks be fair
   And Greta woods be gay,
Yet mickle[1] must the maiden dare
   Would reign my Queen of May!

"Maiden! a nameless life I lead,
   A nameless death I'll die;
The fiend, whose lantern lights the mead
   Were better mate than I!
And when I'm with my comrades met
   Beneath the greenwood bough
What once we were we all forget,
   Nor think what we are now.

Chorus
"Yet Brignal banks are fresh and fair,
   And Greta woods are green,
And you may gather garlands there
   Would grace a summer queen."

SIR WALTER SCOTT

[1] Much.

46

An Old Folk Song

A CARRION crow sat on an oak,
   Fol de riddle, lol de riddle, hi ding do,
Watching a sailor shape his cloak;
   Sing heigh ho, the carrion crow,
   Fol de riddle, lol de riddle, hi ding do.

Wife, bring me my old bent bow,
   Fol de riddle, lol de riddle, hi ding do,
That I may shoot yon carrion crow;
   Sing heigh ho, the carrion crow,
   Fol de riddle, lol de riddle, hi ding do.

The tailor he shot and missed his mark,
   Fol de riddle, lol de riddle, hi ding do,
And shot his own sow through the heart;
   Sing heigh ho, the carrion crow,
   Fol de riddle, lol de riddle, hi ding do.

Wife, bring brandy in a spoon,
   Fol de riddle, lol de riddle, hi ding do,
For our old sow is in a swoon;
   Sing heigh ho, the carrion crow,
   Fol de riddle, lol de riddle, hi ding do.

ANONYMOUS

Kitty of Coleraine

As beautiful Kitty one morning was tripping,
    With a pitcher of milk from the fair of
                             Coleraine,
When she saw me she stumbled, the pitcher it
                             tumbled,
    And all the sweet butter-milk watered the plain.

"O, what shall I do now, 'twas looking at you now,
    Sure, sure, such a pitcher I'll ne'er meet again,
'Twas the pride of my dairy, O, Barney M'Leary,
    You're sent as a plague to the girls of Coleraine."

I sat down beside her,—and gently did chide her,
    That such a misfortune should give her such
                             pain,
A kiss then I gave her,—before I did leave her,
    She vowed for such pleasure she'd break it again.

'Twas hay-making season, I can't tell the reason,
    Misfortunes will never come single,—that's
                             plain,
For, very soon after poor Kitty's disaster,
    The devil a pitcher was whole in Coleraine.

E. LYSAGHT

A Carol

I SING of a maiden
    That is makeles;[1]
King of all kings
    To her son she ches.[2]

He came all so still
    There his mother was,
As dew in April
    That falleth on the grass.

He came all so still
    To his mother's bower,
As dew in April
    That falleth on the flower.

He came all so still
    There his mother lay,
As dew in April
    That falleth on the spray.

Mother and maiden
    Was never none but she;
Well may such a lady
    God's mother be.

ANONYMOUS

[1] Matchless.   [2] Chose.

The Fine Old English Gentleman

I'LL sing you a good old song,
   Made by a good old pate,
Of a fine old English gentleman
   Who had an old estate,
And who kept up his old mansion
   At a bountiful old rate;
With a good old porter to relieve
   The old poor at his gate,
Like a fine old English gentleman
   All of the olden time.

His hall so old was hung around
   With pikes and guns and bows,
And swords, and good old bucklers,
   That had stood some tough old blows;
'Twas there *his worship* held his state
   In doublet and trunk hose,
And quaffed his cup of good old sack,
   To warm his good old nose,
Like a fine old English gentleman
   All of the olden time.

When winter's cold brought frost and snow,
　　He opened house to all;
And though threescore and ten his years,
　　He featly[1] led the ball;
Nor was the houseless wanderer
　　E'er driven from his hall;
For while he feasted all the great,
　　He ne'er forgot the small;
Like a fine old English gentleman
　　All of the olden time.

But time, though old, is strong in flight,
　　And years rolled swiftly by;
And Autumn's falling leaves proclaimed
　　This good old man must die!
He laid him down right tranquilly,
　　Gave up life's latest sigh;
And mournful stillness reigned around,
　　And tears bedewed each eye,
For this fine old English gentleman
　　All of the olden time.

Now surely this is better far
　　Than all the new parade
Of theatres and fancy balls,
　　"At home" and masquerade:
And much more economical,

[1] Nimbly.

For all his bills were paid.
Then leave your new vagaries quite,
   And take up the old trade
Of a fine old English gentleman,
   All of the olden time.

ANONYMOUS

Hunting Song

WAKEN, lords and ladies gay,
   On the mountain dawns the day,
All the jolly chase is here,
With hawk, and horse, and hunting-spear!
Hounds are in their couples yelling,
Hawks are whistling, horns are knelling,
Merrily, merrily, mingle they
   "Waken, lords and ladies gay."

Waken, lords and ladies gay,
The mist has left the mountain grey,
Springlets in the dawn are steaming,
Diamonds on the brake are gleaming:
And foresters have busy been,
To track the buck in thicket green;
Now we come to chant our lay,
   "Waken, lords and ladies gay".

Waken, lords and ladies gay,
To the greenwood haste away;
We can show you where he lies,
Fleet of foot, and tall of size;
We can show the marks he made,
When 'gainst the oak his antlers frayed;
You shall see him brought to bay,
    "Waken, lords and ladies gay."

Louder, louder, chant the lay,
    "Waken, lords and ladies gay"!
Tell them, youth and mirth and glee,
Run a course as well as we;
Time, stern huntsman! who can baulk,
Staunch as hound, and fleet as hawk!
Think of this, and rise with day,
Gentle lords and ladies gay.

SIR WALTER SCOTT

Over Hill, Over Dale

OVER hill, over dale,
    Thorough bush, thorough brier,
Over park, over pale,
    Thorough flood, thorough fire,
I do wander everywhere,
Swifter than the moonè's sphere;

And I serve the fairy queen,
To dew her orbs upon the green:
The cowslips tall her pensioners be;
In their gold coats spots you see;
Those be rubies, fairy favours,
In those freckles live their savours:
I must go seek some dew-drops here,
And hang a pearl in every cowslip's ear.

WILLIAM SHAKESPEARE

Witches' Song

THE owl is abroad, the bat, and the toad,
   And so is the cat-a-mountain,
The ant and the mole sit both in a hole,
   And frog peeps out o' the fountain;
The dogs, they do bay, and the timbrels play,
   The spindle is now a-turning;
The moon it is red, and the stars are fled,
   But all the sky is a-burning:
The ditch is made, and our nails the spade,
With pictures full, of wax, and of wool;
Their livers I stick, with needles quick;
There lacks but the blood, to make up the flood.
   Quickly DAME, then, bring your part in,
   Spur, spur, upon little MARTIN,
   Merrily, merrily, make him sail

A worm in his mouth, and a thorn in's tail,
Fire above, and fire below,
With a whip i' your hand, to make him go.
O, now she's come!
Let all be dumb.

BEN JONSON

The Mermaid

ON Friday morn as we set sail,
    It was not far from land,
O, there I spy'd a fair pretty maid,
    With a comb and a glass in her hand.

        The stormy winds did blow,
            And the raging seas did roar,
        While we poor sailors went to the top,
            And the land-lubbers laid below.

Then up spoke a boy of our gallant ship,
    And a well-speaking boy was he,
"I've a father and a mother in Portsmouth town,
    And this night they weep for me."

    Chorus.

Then up spoke a man of our gallant ship,
    And a well-speaking man was he,
"I married a wife in fair London town,
    And this night she a widow will be."

Chorus.

Then up spoke The Captain of our gallant ship,
    And a valiant man was he,
"For want of a boat we shall be drown'd,
    For she sunk to the bottom of the sea."

Chorus.

The moon shone bright, and the stars gave light,
    And my mother was looking for me,
She might look and weep with watery eyes,
    She might look to the bottom of the sea.

Chorus.

Three times round went our gallant ship,
    And three times round went she,
Three times round went our gallant ship,
    Then she sunk to the bottom of the sea.

Chorus.

ANONYMOUS

PEOPLE

Proud Maisie

Proud Maisie is in the wood,
    Walking so early;
Sweet Robin sits on the bush,
    Singing so rarely.

"Tell me, thou bonny bird,
    When shall I marry me?"
—"When six braw gentlemen
    Kirkward shall carry ye."

"Who makes the bridal bed,
    Birdie, say truly?"
—"The grey-headed sexton
    That delves the grave duly.

"The glow-worm o'er grave and stone
    Shall light thee steady.
The owl from the steeple sing,
    'Welcome, proud lady.'"

SIR WALTER SCOTT

The Scout

DOWN came the horseman
  Through the silent wood,
Like a tide of light
Like an ocean flood.

Conies and foxes,
Every wildwood thing
Crouching in fright,
Heard the hard hooves ring.

Clean as a meteor,
Sharp as folding flame
He circled and vanished
Swift as he came.

RICHARD CHURCH

Song of the Old Mother

I RISE in the dawn, and I kneel and blow
  Till the seed of the fire flicker and glow;
And then I must scrub and bake and sweep
Till stars are beginning to blink and peep:
And the young lie long and dream in their bed
Of the matching of ribbons for bosom and head,
And their day goes over in idleness,
And they sigh if the wind but lift a tress:
  While I must work because I am old,
And the seed of the fire gets feeble and cold.

W. B. YEATS

An Old Woman of the Roads

O, TO have a little house!
    To own the hearth and stool and all!
The heap'd-up sods upon the fire,
The pile of turf against the wall!

To have a clock with weights and chains
And pendulum swinging up and down!
A dresser filled with shining delph,
Speckled and white and blue and brown!

I could be busy all the day
Clearing and sweeping hearth and floor;
And fixing on their shelf again
My white and blue and speckled store!

I could be quiet there at night
Beside the fire and by myself,
Sure of a bed and loth to leave
The ticking clock and the shining delph!

Och! but I'm weary of mist and dark,
And roads where there's never a house nor bush,
And tired I am of bog and road
And the crying wind and the lonesome hush!

And I am praying to God on high,
And I am praying Him night and day,
For a little house—a house of my own—
Out of the wind's and the rain's way.

PADRAIC COLUM

Alone

A VERY old woman
    Lives in yon house.
The squeak of the cricket,
The stir of the mouse,
Are all she knows
Of the earth and us.

Once she was young,
Would dance and play,
Like many another
Young popinjay;
And run to her mother
At dusk of day.

And colours bright
She delighted in;
The fiddle to hear,
And to lift her chin,
And sing as small
As a twittering wren.

But age apace
Comes at last to all;
And a lone house filled
With the cricket's call;
And the scampering mouse
In the hollow wall.

WALTER DE LA MARE

The Fiddler of Dooney

WHEN I play on my fiddle in Dooney
        Folk dance like a wave of the sea;
My cousin is priest in Kilvarnet,
My brother in Moharabuiee.

I pass'd my brother and cousin:
They read in their books of prayer;
I read in my book of songs
I bought at the Sligo fair.

When we come at the end of time,
To Peter sitting in state,
He will smile on the three old spirits,
But call me first through the gate;

For the good are always the merry,
Save by an evil chance;
And the merry love the fiddle,
And the merry love to dance:

And when the folk there spy me,
They will all come up to me,
With "Here is the fiddler of Dooney!"
And dance like a wave of the sea.

W. B. YEATS

Meg Merrilies

OLD Meg she was a gipsy,
   And lived upon the moors:
Her bed it was the brown heath turf,
   And her house was out of doors.
Her apples were swart blackberries,
   Her currants, pods o' broom;
Her wine was dew of the wild white rose,
   Her book a churchyard tomb.

Her brothers were the craggy hills,
   Her sisters larchen trees;
Alone with her great family
   She lived as she did please.
No breakfast had she many a morn,
   No dinner many a noon,
And, 'stead of supper, she would stare
   Full hard against the moon.

But every morn, of woodbine fresh
   She made her garlanding,
And, every night, the dark glen yew
   She wove, and she would sing.
And with her fingers, old and brown,
   She plaited mats of rushes,
And gave them to the cottagers
   She met among the bushes.

Old Meg was brave as Margaret Queen,
   And tall as Amazon;
An old red blanket cloak she wore,
   A chip-hat[1] had she on:
God rest her agèd bones somewhere!
   She died full long agone!

JOHN KEATS

Allen-a-Dale

ALLEN-A-DALE has no fagot for burning,
   Allen-a-Dale has no furrow for turning,
Allen-a-Dale has no fleece for the spinning,
Yet Allen-a-Dale has red gold for the winning!
Come, read me my riddle! come, hearken my tale!
And tell me the craft of bold Allen-a-Dale.

The Baron of Ravensworth prances in pride,
And he views his domains upon Arkindale side,
The mere for his net, and the land for his game,
The chase for the wild, and the park for the tame,
Yet the fish of the lake and the deer of the vale,
Are less free to Lord Dacre than Allen-a-Dale!

[1] A hat made of thin strips of woody fibre.

Allen-a-Dale was ne'er belted a knight,
Though his spear be as sharp, and his blade be as
                                    bright;

Allen-a-Dale is no baron or lord,
Yet twenty tall yeomen will draw at his word;
And the best of our nobles his bonnet will vail,
Who at Rere-cross on Stanmore meets Allen-a-Dale.

Allen-a-Dale to his wooing is come;
The mother, she asked of his household and home;
"Though the castle of Richmond stands fair on
                                    the hill,
My hall," quoth bold Allen, "shows gallanter still;
'Tis the blue vault of heaven, with its crescent so
                                    pale,
And with all its bright spangles!" said Allen-a-Dale.

The father was steel, and the mother was stone;
They lifted the latch, and they bade him be gone;
But loud, on the morrow, their wail and their cry:
He had laughed on the lass with his bonny black
                                    eye;

And she fled to the forest to hear a love-tale,
And the youth it was told by was Allen-a-Dale!

SIR WALTER SCOTT

Pocahontas

WEARIED arm and broken sword
    Wage in vain the desperate fight;
Round him press a countless horde,
  He is but a single knight.
Hark! a cry of triumph shrill
   Through the wilderness resounds,
   As, with twenty bleeding wounds,
Sinks the warrior, fighting still.

Now they heap the fatal pyre,
   And the torch of death they light:
Ah! 'tis hard to die of fire!
   Who will shield the captive knight?
Round the stake with fiendish cry
   Wheel and dance the savage crowd,
   Cold the victim's mien and proud,
And his breast is bared to die.

Who will shield the fearless heart?
   Who avert the murderous blade?
From the throng, with sudden start,
   See there springs an Indian maid.
Quick she stands before the knight;
   "Loose the chain, unbind the ring;
   I am daughter of the King,
And I claim the Indian right!"

Dauntlessly aside she flings
    Lifted axe and thirsty knife;
Fondly to his heart she clings,
    And her bosom guards his life!
In the woods of Powhattan,
    Still 'tis told, by Indian fires,
    How a daughter of their sires
Saved the captive Englishman.

W. M. THACKERAY

The Horse-Trough

CLOUDS of children round the trough
    Splash and clatter in the sun:
Their clouted shoes are mostly off,
And some are quarrelling, and one
Cools half her face, nose downward bubbling,
Wetting her clothes and never troubling;
Bobble, bobble, bobble there
Till bubbles like young earthquakes heave
The orange island of her hair,

66

And tidal waves run up her sleeve;
Another's tanned as brown as bistre;
Another ducks his little sister,
And all are mixed in such a crowd
And tell their separate joys so loud
That who can be this silent one,
This dimpled, pensive, baby one?
—She sits the sunny steps so still
For hours, trying hard to kill
One fly at least of those that buzz
So cannily . . .
                    And then she does.

RICHARD HUGHES

THE COUNTRY LIFE

The Scarecrow

ALL winter through I bow my head
    Beneath the driving rain;
The North wind powders me with snow
    And blows me black again;
At midnight 'neath a maze of stars
    I flame with glittering rime,
And stand, above the stubble, stiff
    As mail at morning-prime.
But when that child, called Spring, and all
    His host of children, come,
Scattering their buds and dew upon
    These acres of my home,
Some rapture in my rags awakes;
    I lift void eyes and scan
The skies for crows, those ravening foes,
    Of my strange master, Man.
I watch him striding lank behind
    His clashing team, and know
Soon will the wheat swish body high
    Where once lay sterile snow;
Soon shall I gaze across a sea
    Of sun-begotten grain,
Which my unflinching watch hath sealed
    For harvest once again.

WALTER DE LA MARE

The Brook

I COME from haunts of coot and hern,
   I make a sudden sally,
And sparkle out among the fern,
   To bicker down a valley.

By thirty hills I hurry down,
   Or slip between the ridges,
By twenty thorps, a little town,
   And half a hundred bridges.

Till last by Philip's farm I flow
   To join the brimming river,
For men may come and men may go,
   But I go on for ever.

I chatter over stony ways,
   In little sharps and trebles,
I bubble into eddying bays,
   I babble on the pebbles.

With many a curve my banks I fret
   By many a field and fallow,
And many a fairy foreland set
   With willow-weed and mallow.

I chatter, chatter, as I flow
   To join the brimming river,
For men may come and men may go,
   But I go on for ever.

I wind about, and in and out,
　　With here a blossom sailing,
And here and there a lusty trout,
　　And here and there a grayling,

And here and there a foamy flake
　　Upon me, as I travel
With many a silvery waterbreak
　　Above the golden gravel,

And draw them all along, and flow
　　To join the brimming river,
For men may come and men may go
　　But I go on for ever.

I steal by lawns and grassy plots,
　　I slide by hazel covers;
I move the sweet forget-me-nots
　　That grow for happy lovers.

I slip, I slide, I gloom, I glance,
　　Among my skimming swallows;
I make the netted sunbeam dance
　　Against my sandy shallows.

I murmur under moon and stars
　　In brambly wildernesses;
I linger by my shingly bars;
　　I loiter round my cresses;

And out again I curve and flow
    To join the brimming river,
For men may come and men may go,
    But I go on for ever.

ALFRED, LORD TENNYSON

A Song of Enchantment

A SONG of Enchantment I sang me there,
    In a green-green wood, by waters fair,
Just as the words came up to me
I sang it under the wild wood tree.

Widdershins[1] turned I, singing it low,
Watching the wild birds come and go;
No cloud in the deep dark blue to be seen
Under the thick-thatched branches green.

Twilight came: silence came:
The planet of Evening's silver flame;
By darkening paths I wandered through
Thickets trembling with drops of dew.

But the music is lost and the words are gone
Of the song I sang as I sat alone,
Ages and ages have fallen on me—
On the wood and the pool and the elder tree.

WALTER DE LA MARE

[1] Away from the sun's direction.

The Night

THE Night was creeping on the ground!
    She crept and did not make a sound,

Until she reached the tree: And then
She covered it, and stole again

Along the grass beside the wall!
I heard the rustle of her shawl

As she threw blackness everywhere
Upon the sky, the ground, the air,

And in the room where I was hid!
But, no matter what she did

To everything that was without,
She could not put my candle out!

So I stared at the Night! And she
Stared back solemnly at me!

JAMES STEPHENS

Roadways

ONE road leads to London,
    One road runs to Wales,
My road leads me seawards
    To the white dipping sails.

One road leads to the river,
    As it goes singing slow;
My road leads to shipping,
    Where the bronzed sailors go.

Leads me, lures me, calls me
    To salt green tossing sea;
A road without earth's road-dust
    Is the right road for me.

A wet road heaving, shining,
    And wild with seagulls' cries,
A mad salt sea-wind blowing
    The salt spray in my eyes.

My road calls me, lures me
    West, east, south, and north;
Most roads lead men homewards,
    My road leads me forth.

To add more miles to the tally
    Of grey miles left behind,
In quest of that one beauty
    God put me here to find.

JOHN MASEFIELD

March

THE cock is crowing,
    The stream is flowing,
The small birds twitter,
The lake doth glitter,
The green field sleeps in the sun:
    The oldest and youngest
    Are at work with the strongest;
    The cattle are grazing,
    Their heads never raising;
There are forty feeding like one!

    Like an army defeated
    The snow hath retreated,
    And now doth fare ill
    On the top of the bare hill;
The ploughboy is whooping—anon—anon:
    There's joy on the mountains;
    There's life in the fountains;
    Small clouds are sailing,
    Blue sky prevailing;
The rain is over and gone!

WILLIAM WORDSWORTH

Autumn

THE thistle down's flying, though the winds are
                                            all still,
On the green grass now lying, now mounting the
                                            hill,
The spring from the fountain now boils like a pot;
Through stones past the counting it bubbles red-hot.

The ground parched and cracked is like overbaked
                                            bread,
The greensward all wracked is, bents dried up
                                            and dead.
The fallow fields glitter like water indeed,
And gossamers twitter flung from weed unto weed.

Hill tops like hot iron glitter bright in the sun,
And the rivers we're eyeing burn to gold as they
                                            run;
Burning hot is the ground, liquid gold is the air;
Whoever looks round sees Eternity there.

JOHN CLARE

75

Ice

THE North Wind sighed:
    And in a trice,
What was water
Now is ice.

What sweet rippling
Water was,
Now bewitched is
Into glass:

White and brittle
Where is seen
The prisoned milfoil's
Tender green.

Clear and ringing,
With sun aglow,
Where the boys sliding
And skating go.

Now furred's each stick
And stalk and blade
With crystals out of
Dewdrops made.

Worms and ants,
Flies, snails and bees
Keep close house-guard
Lest they freeze.

Oh, with how sad
And solemn an eye
Each fish stares up
Into the sky.

In dread lest his
Wide watery home
At night shall solid
Ice become.

WALTER DE LA MARE

The West Wind

IT'S a warm wind, the west wind, full of birds'
                                            cries;
I never hear the west wind but tears are in my
                                            eyes.
For it comes from the west lands, the old brown
                                            hills,
And April's in the west wind, and daffodils.

It's a fine land, the west land, for hearts as tired
                                            as mine,
Apple orchards blossom there, and the air's like
                                            wine.
There is cool green grass there, where men may
                                            lie at rest,
And the thrushes are in song there, fluting from
                                            the nest.

"Will you not come home, brother? Ye have been
                                    long away,
It's April, and blossom time, and white is the may;
And bright is the sun, brother, and warm is the
                                    rain,—
Will you not come home, brother, home to us
                                    again?

"The young corn is green, brother, where the
                                    rabbits run,
It's blue sky, and white clouds, and warm rain
                                    and sun,
It's song to a man's soul, brother, fire to a man's
                                    brain,
To hear the wild bees and see the merry spring
                                    again.

"Larks are singing in the west, brother, above the
                                    green wheat,
So will you not come home, brother, and rest your
                                    tired feet?
I've a balm for bruised hearts, brother, sleep for
                                    aching eyes,"
Says the warm wind, the west wind, full of birds'
                                    cries.

It's the white road westwards is the road I must
                                                    tread
To the green grass, the cool grass, and rest for
                                              heart and head,
To the violets and the warm hearts and the
                                              thrushes' song,
In the fine land, the west land, the land where I
                                                    belong.

JOHN MASEFIELD

A Boy's Song

WHERE the pools are bright and deep,
    Where the gray trout lies asleep,
Up the river and over the lea,
That's the way for Billy and me.

Where the blackbird sings the latest,
Where the hawthorn blooms the sweetest,
Where the nestlings chirp and flee,
That's the way for Billy and me.

Where the mowers mow the cleanest,
Where the hay lies thick and greenest,
There to track the homeward bee,
That's the way for Billy and me.

Where the hazel bank is steepest,
Where the shadow falls the deepest,
Where the clustering nuts fall free,
That's the way for Billy and me.

This I know, I love to play,
Through the meadow, among the hay,
Up the water and over the lea,
That's the way for Billy and me.

JAMES HOGG

The Echoing Green

THE sun does arise
   And make happy the skies;
The merry bells ring
To welcome the Spring,
The skylark and thrush,
The birds of the bush,
Sing louder around
To the bells' cheerful sound,
While our sports shall be seen
On the Echoing Green.

Old John, with white hair,
Does laugh away care,
Sitting under the oak,
Among the old folk,
They laugh at our play,
And soon they all say:
"Such, such were the joys
When we all—girls and boys—
In our youth-time were seen
On the Echoing Green."

Till the little ones, weary,
No more can be merry:
The sun does descend,
And our sports have an end,
Round the laps of their mothers
Many sisters and brothers,
Like birds in their nest,
Are ready for rest,
And sport no more seen
On the darkening Green.

WILLIAM BLAKE

The River

THE silver Severn water
 It winds its way at ease
Across the amber pebbles,
Beneath the alder trees,
And all day long its quiet voice
Is sweet to me as my heart's choice.

The dark pool holds the otter;
We hunted him at morn
When dewy, airy gossamers
Were hung on every thorn,
But though we saw his silver chain
Till noon we holloaed there in vain.

Then when the orchard grasses
Were flecked with shade and sun,
Barefooted to the water
We boys and girls would run,
And leaping there would plunge and swim
Through broken lights and shadows dim.

Ah, where are now the voices
That echoed on those shores?
And where the jolly boatmen
Who dipped their yellow oars?
The sunset lingers in the sky,
But still the changing stream runs by.

EILUNED LEWIS

After Reading in a Letter
Proposals for Building a Cottage

BESIDE a runnel build my shed,
  With stubbles covered o'er;
Let broad oaks o'er its chimney spread,
  And grass-plats grace the door.

The door may open with a string,
  So that it closes tight;
And locks would be a wanted thing
  To keep out thieves at night.

A little garden, not too fine,
  Enclose with painted pales;
And woodbines, round the cot to twine,
  Pin to the wall with nails.

Let hazels grow, and spindling sedge
  Bend bowering overhead;
Dig old man's beard from woodland hedge
  To twine a summer shade.

Beside the threshold sods provide,
  And build a summer seat;
Plant sweet-briar bushes by its side,
  And flowers that blossom sweet.

I love the sparrows' ways to watch
    Upon the cotters' sheds,
So here and there pull out the thatch
    That they may hide their heads.

Anu as the sweeping swallows stop
    Their flights along the green,
Leave holes within the chimney-top
    To paste their nest between.

Stick shelves and cupboards round the hut,
    In all the holes and nooks;
Nor in the corner fail to put
    A cupboard for the books.

Along the floor some sand I'll **sift**,
    To make it fit to live in;
And then I'll thank ye for the gift,
    As something worth the giving.

JOHN CLARE

The Deserted House

THERE'S no smoke in the chimney,
  And the rain beats on the floor;
There's no glass in the window,
  There's no wood in the door;
The heather grows behind the house,
  And the sand lies before.

No hand hath trained the ivy,
  The walls are gray and bare;
The boats upon the sea sail by,
  Nor ever tarry there.
No beast of the field comes nigh,
  Nor any bird of the air.

MARY COLERIDGE

The Fairy Queen

COME follow, follow me,
  You, fairy elves that be:
Which circle on the greene,
  Come follow Mab your queene.
Hand in hand let's dance around,
For this place is fairy ground.

  When mortals are at rest,
  And snoring in their nest;
  Unheard, and unespied,
  Through keyholes do we glide;
Over tables, stools, and shelves,
We trip it with our fairy elves.

And, if the house be foul
With platter, dish, or bowl,
Upstairs we nimbly creep,
And find the sluts asleep;
There we pinch their armes and thighes;
None escapes, nor none espies.

But if the house be swept,
And from uncleanness kept,
We praise the household maid,
And duly she is paid:
For we use before we go
To drop a tester[1] in her shoe.

Upon a mushroom's head
Our tablecloth we spread;
A grain of rye, or wheat,
Is manchet,[2] which we eat;
Pearly drops of dew we drink
In acorn cups filled to the brink.

The brains of nightingales,
With unctuous fat of snails,
Between two cockles stewed,
Is meat that's easily chewed;
Tails of worms, and marrow of mice,
Do make a dish that's wondrous nice.

[1] Sixpence.
[2] A small loaf.

The grasshopper, gnat, and fly,
Serve for our minstrelsie;
Grace said, we dance awhile,
And so the time beguile:
And if the moon doth hide her head,
The glow-worm lights us home to bed.

On tops of dewy grass
So nimbly do we pass;
The young and tender stalk
Ne'er bends when we do walk:
Yet in the morning may be seen
Where we the night before have been.

ANONYMOUS

Robin Goodfellow

FROM Oberon, in fairy land,
   The king of ghosts and shadows there,
Mad Robin I, at his command,
   Am sent to view the night-sports here.
      What revel rout
      Is kept about,
  In every corner where I go,
   I will o'ersee, and merry be,
And make good sport, with ho, ho, ho!

More swift than lightning can I fly
   About their aery welkin soon,
And, in a minute's space, descry
   Each thing that's done below the moon.
      There's not a hag
      Or ghost shall wag,
  Or cry, 'ware goblins! where I go;
   But Robin I their feats will spy,
And send them home, with ho, ho, ho!

Whene'er such wanderers I meet,
   As from their night-sports they trudge home,
With counterfeiting voice I greet,
   And call them on with me to roam:
      Through woods, through lakes;
      Through bogs, through brakes;
  Or else, unseen, with them I go,
   All in the nick to play some trick,
And frolic it, with ho, ho, ho!

Sometimes I meet them like a man,
    Sometimes an ox, sometimes a hound;
And to a horse I turn me can,
    To trip and trot about them round.
        But if to ride
        My back they stride,
More swift than wind away I go,
    O'er hedge and lands,
            through pools and ponds,
I hurry, laughing, ho, ho, ho!

When lads and lasses merry be,
    With possets and with junkets fine;
Unseen of all the company,
    I eat their cakes and sip their wine!
        And, to make sport,
        I puff and snort;
And out the candles I do blow:
    The maids I kiss; they shriek—Who's this?
I answer naught but ho, ho, ho!

Yet now and then, the maids to please,
    At midnight I card up their wool;
And, while they sleep and take their ease,
    With wheel to threads their flax I pull.
        I grind at mill
        Their malt up still;
I dress their hemp; I spin their tow;
    If any 'wake, and would me take,
I wend me, laughing, ho, ho, ho!

When any need to borrow aught,
  We lend them what they do require:
And, for the use demand we nought;
  Our own is all we do desire.
        If to repay
        They do delay,
  Abroad amongst them then I go,
    And night by night, I them affright
  With pinchings, dreams, and ho, ho, ho!

When lazie queans have nought to do,
  But study how to cog and lye:
To make debate and mischief too,
  'Twixt one another secretly:
        I mark their gloze,
        And it disclose
  To them whom they have wrongèd so:
    When I have done, I get me gone,
  And leave them scolding, ho, ho, ho!

When men do traps and engines set
  In loop-holes where the vermin creep,
Whom from their folds and houses get
  Their ducks and geese, and lambs and sheep;
        I spy the gin
        And enter in,
  And seem a vermin taken so;
    But when they there approach me near,
  I leap out laughing, ho, ho, ho!

By wells and rills, in meadows green,
　　We nightly dance our heyday guise;[1]
And to our fairy king and queen
　　We chant our moonlight minstrelsies.
　　　　When larks 'gin sing,
　　　　Away we fling;
And babes new born steal as we go;
　　And elf in bed we leave instead,
And wend us laughing, ho, ho, ho!

From hag-bred Merlin's time have I
　　Thus nightly revelled to and fro;
And for my pranks men call me by
　　The name of Robin Good-fellòw.
　　　　Fiends, ghosts, and sprites,
　　　　Who haunt the nights,
The hags and goblins do we know;
　　And beldames old my feats have told,
So vale, vale; ho, ho, ho!

ANONYMOUS

[1] Or hey-de-guys, country dances.

TALES OF LONG AGO

Puck's Song

SEE you the dimpled track that runs,
    All hollow through the wheat?
O that was where they hauled the guns
    That smote King Philip's fleet.

See you our little mill that clacks,
    So busy by the brook?
She has ground her corn and paid her tax
    Ever since Doomsday Book.

See you our stilly woods of oak,
    And the dread ditch beside?
O that was where the Saxons broke,
    On the day that Harold died.

See you the windy levels spread
    About the gates of Rye?
O that was where the Northmen fled,
    When Alfred's ships came by.

See you our pastures wide and lone,
    Where the red oxen browse?
O there was a City thronged and known,
    Ere London boasted a house.

And see you, after rain, the trace
    Of mound and ditch and wall?
O that was a Legion's camping-place,
    When Cæsar sailed from Gaul.

And see you marks that show and fade,
    Like shadows on the Downs?
O they are the lines the Flint Men made,
    To guard their wondrous towns.

Trackway and Camp and City lost,
    Salt Marsh where now is corn;
Old Wars, old Peace, old Arts that cease,
    And so was England born.

She is not any common Earth,
    Water or wood or air,
But Merlin's Isle of Gramarye,[1]
    Where you and I will fare.

RUDYARD KIPLING

[1] Magic, glamour.

Robin Hood and the Bishop of Hereford

COME, Gentlemen all, and listen a while;
    A story I'll to you unfold—
How Robin Hood servèd the Bishop,
When he robb'd him of his gold.

As it befell in merry Barnsdale,
And under the green-wood tree,
The Bishop of Hereford was to come by,
With all his companye.

"Come, kill a ven'son," said bold Robin Hood,
"Come, kill me a good fat deer;
The Bishop's to dine with me to-day,
And he shall pay well for his cheer.

"We'll kill a fat ven'son," said bold Robin Hood,
"And dress 't by the highway-side,
And narrowly watch for the Bishop,
Lest some other way he should ride."

He dress'd himself up in shepherd's attire,
With six of his men also;
And the Bishop of Hereford came thereby,
As about the fire they did go.

"What matter is this?" said the Bishop;
"Or for whom do you make this a-do?
Or why do you kill the King's ven'son,
When your company is so few?"

"We are shepherds," said bold Robin Hood,
"And we keep sheep all the year;
And we are disposed to be merry this day,
And to kill of the King's fat deer."

"You are brave fellowes," said the Bishop,
"And the King of your doings shall know;
Therefore make haste, come along with me,
For before the King you shall go."

"O pardon, O pardon," says bold Robin Hood,
"O pardon, I thee pray!
For it never becomes your lordship's coat
To take so many lives away."

"No pardon, no pardon!" the Bishop says;
"No pardon I thee owe;
Therefore make haste, come along with me,
For before the King you shall go."

Robin set his back against a tree,
And his foot against a thorn,
And from underneath his shepherd's coat
He pull'd out a bugle horn.

He put the little end to his mouth,
And a loud blast did he blow,
Till threescore and ten of bold Robin's men,
Came running all on a row;

All making obeisance to bold Robin Hood;
—'Twas a comely sight for to see:
"What matter, my master," said Little John,
"That you blow so hastilye?"—

"O here is the Bishop of Hereford,
And no pardon we shall have."—
"Cut off his head, master," said Little John,
"And throw him into his grave."—

"O pardon, O pardon," said the Bishop,
"O pardon, I thee pray!
For if I had known it had been you,
I'd have gone some other way."—

"No pardon, no pardon!" said Robin Hood;
"No pardon I thee owe;
Therefore make haste, come along with me,
For to merry Barnsdale you shall go."

Then Robin has taken the Bishop's hand
And led him to merry Barnsdale;
He made him to stay and sup with him that night,
And to drink wine, beer and ale.

"Call in the reckoning," said the Bishop,
"For methinks it grows wondrous high."—
"Lend me your purse, Bishop," said Little John,
"And I'll tell you by-and-by."

Then Little John took the Bishop's cloak,
And spread it upon the ground,
And out of the Bishop's portmantua
He told three hundred pound.

"So now let him go," said Robin Hood,
Said Little John, "That may not be;
For I vow and protest he shall sing us a mass
Before that he go from me."

Robin Hood took the Bishop by the hand,
And bound him fast to a tree,
And made him to sing a mass, God wot,
To him and his yeomandrye.

Then Robin Hood brought him through the wood
And caus̀ed the music to play,
And he made the Bishop to dance in his boots,
And they set him on 's dapple-grey,
And they gave the tail within his hand—
And glad he could so get away!

ANONYMOUS

Robin Hood and the Butcher

COME, all you brave gallants, and listen a while,
    That are in the bowers within;
For of Robin Hood, that archer good,
    A song I intend for to sing.

Upon a time it chancèd so
    Bold Robin in forest did spy
A jolly butchèr, with a bonny fine mare,
    With his flesh to the market did hye.

"Good morrow, good fellow!" said jolly Robìn,
    "What food hast? tell unto me;
And thy trade to me tell, and
               where thou dost dwell,
    For I like well thy company."

The butcher he answered jolly Robìn:
    "No matter where I dwell;
For a butcher I am, and to Nottingham
    I am going, my flesh to sell."

"What price thy flesh?" said jolly Robìn,
    "Come, tell it soon unto me;
And the price of thy mare, be she never so dear,
    For a butcher fain would I be."

"The price of my flesh," the butcher replied,
    "I soon will tell unto thee;
With my bonny mare, and they are not dear,
    Four mark thou must give unto me."

"Four mark I will give thee," said jolly Robìn,
      "Four mark it shall be thy fee;
Thy money come count, and let me mount,
      For a butcher I fain would be."

Now Robin he is to Nottingham gone,
      His butcher's trade for to begin;
With good intent, to the Sheriff he went,
      And there he took up his inn.

When other butchers they opened their meat,
      Bold Robin he then begun;
But how for to sell he knew not well,
      For a butcher he was but young.

When other butchers no meat could sell,
      Robin got both gold and fee;
For he sold more meat for one penny
      Than others could do for three.

But when he sold his meat so fast,
      No butcher by him could thrive;
For he sold more meat for one penny
      Than others could do for five.

Which made the butchers of Nottingham
      To study as they did stand,
Saying, surely he was some prodigal,
      That had sold his father's land.

The butchers they stepped to jolly Robìn,
    Acquainted with him for to be;
"Come, brother," one said, "we be all of one trade
    Come, will you go dine with me?"

"Accurst of his heart," said jolly Robìn,
    "That a butcher doth deny!
I will go with you, my brethren true,
    And as fast as I can hie."

But when to the Sheriff's house they came,
    To dinner they hied apace,
And Robin Hood he the man must be
    Before them all to say grace.

"Pray God bless us all," said jolly Robìn,
    "And our meat within this place;
A cup of sack good, to nourish our blood,
    And so I do end my grace.

"Come fill us more wine," said jolly Robìn,
    "Let us merry be while we do stay;
For wine and good cheer, be it never so dear,
    I vow I the reckoning will pay.

"Come, brothers, be merry," said jolly Robìn,
    "Let us drink, and never give o'er;
For the shot I will pay, ere I go my way,
    If it cost me five pounds and more."

"This is a mad blade," the butchers then said;
    Says the Sheriff, "He's some prodigal,
That his land has sold, for silver and gold,
    And meaneth to spend it all."

"Hast thou any horn-beasts," the Sheriff inquired,
    "Good fellow, to sell unto me?"—
"Yea, a plenty I have, good Master Sheriff,
    I have hundreds two or three.

"And a hundred acre of good free land,
    An' it please you go for to see;
And I'll make you as good assurance of it
    As ever my father made me."

The Sheriff he saddled a good palfrey,
    With three hundred pound in gold,
And away he went with bold Robin Hood,
    His horned beasts to behold.

Away then the Sheriff and Robin did ride,
    To the forest of merry Sherwood;
Then the Sheriff did say, "God bless us this day
    From a man they call Robin Hood!"

But when that a little further they came,
    Bold Robin he chanced to spy
A hundred head of the good red deer,
    Come tripping the Sheriff full nigh.

"How like you my horn'd beasts, Master Sheriff?
    They be fat and fair for to see;"
"I tell thee, good fellow, I would I were gone,
    For I like not thy company."

Then Robin he set his horn to his mouth,
    And blew out blastès three;
Then quickly anon there came Little John,
    And all his company.

"What is your will?" then said Little John,
    "Good master come tell it to me;"
"I have brought hither the Sheriff of Nottingham,
    This day to dine with thee."

"He is welcome to me," then said Little John,
    "I hope he will honestly pay;
I know he has gold, if it be but well told,
    Will serve us to drink a whole day."

Robin Hood took his mantle from his back,
    And laid it upon the ground,
And out of the Sheriff's portmantle
    He told three hundred pound.

Then Robin he brought him through the wood,
    Set him on his dapple grey:
"O have me commended, good sir, to your
                            wife!"—
    So Robin went laughing away.

ANONYMOUS

Cock Up Your Beaver

WHEN first my brave Johnnie lad
    Came to this town,
He had a blue bonnet
    That wanted the crown;
But now he has gotten
    A hat and a feather,—
Hey, brave Johnnie lad,
    Cock up your beaver!

Cock up your beaver,
    And cock it fu' sprush,[1]
We'll over the border
    And gie them a brush:
There's somebody there
    We'll teach better behaviour—
Hey, brave Johnnie lad,
    Cock up your beaver!

ROBERT BURNS

[1] Spruce, brisk.

103

Saint Brandan

SAINT BRANDAN sails the northern main;
   The brotherhood of saints are glad.
He greets them once, he sails again.
So late!—such storms!—The Saint is mad!

He heard across the howling seas
Chime convent bells on wintry nights,
He saw on spray-swept Hebrides
Twinkle the monastery lights;

But north, still north, Saint Brandan steer'd;
And now no bells, no convents more!
The hurtling Polar lights are near'd,
The sea without a human shore.

At last—(it was the Christmas night,
Stars shone after a day of storm)—
He sees float past an iceberg white,
And on it—Christ!—a living form!

That furtive mien, that scowling eye,
Of hair that red and tufted fell—
It is—Oh, where shall Brandan fly?—
The traitor Judas, out of hell!

Palsied with terror, Brandan sate;
The moon was bright, the iceberg near.
He hears a voice sigh humbly: "Wait!
By high permission I am here.

"One moment wait, thou holy man!
On earth my crime, my death, they knew;
My name is under all men's ban;
Ah, tell them of my respite too!

"Tell them, one blessed Christmas night—
(It was the first after I came,
Breathing self-murder, frenzy, spite,
To rue my guilt in endless flame)—

"I felt, as I in torment lay
'Mid the souls plagued by heavenly power,
An angel touch mine arm, and say:
Go hence, and cool thyself an hour!

" 'Ah, whence this mercy, Lord?' I said.
The Leper recollect, said he,
Who ask'd the passers-by for aid,
In Joppa, and thy charity.

"Then I remember'd how I went,
In Joppa, through the public street,
One morn, when the sirocco spent
Its storms of dust, with burning heat;

"And in the street a Leper sate,
Shivering with fever, naked, old;
Sand raked his sores from heel to pate,
The hot wind fever'd him five-fold.

"He gazed upon me as I pass'd,
And murmur'd: *Help me, or I die!*—
To the poor wretch my cloak I cast,
Saw him look eased, and hurried by.

"Oh, Brandan, think what grace divine,
What blessing must true goodness shower,
If semblance of it faint, like mine,
Hath such inestimable power!

"Well-fed, well-clothed, well-friended, I
Did that chance act of good, that one!
Then went my way to kill and lie—
Forgot my good as soon as done.

"That germ of kindness, in the womb
Of mercy caught, did not expire;
Outlives my guilt, outlives my doom,
And friends me in the pit of fire.

"Once every year, when carols wake,
On earth, the Christmas night's repose,
Arising from the sinners' lake,
I journey to these healing snows.

"I stanch with ice my burning breast,
With silence balm my whirling brain.
O Brandan! to this hour of rest,
That Joppan leper's ease was pain!"—

Tears started to Saint Brandan's eyes;
He bow'd his head; he breathed a prayer.
When he look'd up—tenantless lies
The iceberg in the frosty air!

MATTHEW ARNOLD

The Danes

THEIR sails, as black as a starless night,
   Came moving on, with a sullen might;
Rows of gleaming shields there hung,
Over the gunwales in order slung;
And the broad black banners fluttered and flapped
Like raven's pinions, as dipped and lapped
The Norsemen's galleys; their axes shone;

Every Dane had a hauberk on—
Glittering gold; how each robber lord
Waved in the air his threatening sword!
One long swift rush through surf and foam
And they leapt, ere the rolling wave had gone,
On our Saxon shore, their new-found home.

GEORGE WALTER THORNBURY

Heather Ate

From the bonny bells of heather
　　They brewed a drink long-syne,
Was sweeter far than honey,
　　Was stronger far than wine.
They brewed it and they drank it,
　　And lay in a blessed swound
For days and days together
　　In their dwellings underground.

There rose a king in Scotland,
　　A fell man to his foes,
He smote the Picts in battle,
　　He hunted them like roes.
Over miles of the red mountain
　　He hunted as they fled,
And strewed the dwarfish bodies
　　Of the dying and the dead.

Summer came in the country,
　　Red was the heather bell;
But the manner of the brewing
　　Was none alive to tell.
In graves that were like children's
　　On many a mountain head,
The Brewsters of the Heather
　　Lay numbered with the dead.

The king in the red moorland
    Rode on a summer's day;
And the bees hummed, and the curlews
    Cried beside the way.
The king rode, and was angry,
    Black was his brow and pale,
To rule in a land of heather
    And lack the Heather Ale.

It fortuned that his vassals,
    Riding free on the heath,
Came on a stone that was fallen
    And vermin hid beneath.
Rudely plucked from their hiding,
    Never a word they spoke:
A son and his aged father—
    Last of the dwarfish folk.

The king sat high on his charger,
    He looked on the little men;
And the dwarfish and swarthy couple
    Looked at the king again.
Down by the shore he had them;
    And there on the giddy brink—
"I will give you life, ye vermin,
    For the secret of the drink."

There stood the son and father
   And they looked high and low;
The heather was red around them,
   The sea rumbled below.
And up and spoke the father,
   Shrill was his voice to hear:
"I have a word in private,
   A word for the royal ear.

"Life is dear to the aged,
   And honour a little thing;
I would gladly sell the secret,"
   Quoth the Pict to the king.
His voice was small as a sparrow's,
   And shrill and wonderful clear;
"I would gladly sell my secret,
   Only my son I fear.

"For life is a little matter
   And death is nought to the young;
And I dare not sell my honour
   Under the eye of my son.
Take *him*, O king, and bind him,
   And cast him far in the deep;
And it's I will tell the secret
   That I have sworn to keep."

They took the son and bound him,
   Neck and heels in a thong,
And a lad took him and swung him,
   And flung him far and strong,
And the sea swallowed his body,
   Like that of a child of ten;—
And there on the cliff stood the father,
   Last of the dwarfish men.

"True was the word I told you:
   Only my son I feared;
For I doubt the sapling courage
   That goes without the beard.
But now in vain is the torture,
   Fire shall never avail:
Here dies in my bosom
   The secret of Heather Ale."

ROBERT LOUIS STEVENSON

A Farewell

Go fetch to me a pint o' wine,
   An' fill it in a silver tassie;
That I may drink before I go
   A service to my bonnie lassie:
The boat rocks at the pier o' Leith,
   Fu' loud the wind blaws frae the ferry,
The ship rides by the Berwick-law,
   And I maun leave my bonnie Mary.

The trumpets sound, the banners fly,
   The glittering spears are rankèd ready;
The shouts o' war are heard afar,
   The battle closes thick and bloody;
But it's no the roar o' sea or shore
   Wad make me langer wish to tarry;
Nor shout o' war that's heard afar—
   It's leaving thee, my bonnie Mary.

ROBERT BURNS

The Old Navy

THE captain stood on the carronade:[1] "First
                     lieutenant," says he,
"Send all my merry men aft here, for they must
                     list to me;
I haven't the gift of the gab, my sons—because
                     I'm bred to the sea;
That ship there is a Frenchman, who means to
                     fight with we.
   And odds bobs, hammer and tongs, long as
                     I've been to sea,
   I've fought 'gainst every odds—and I've
                     gained the victory!

[1] Naval gun first cast at Carron, near Edinburgh.

"That ship there is a Frenchman, and if we don't
                        take she,
'Tis a thousand bullets to one, that she will
                        capture we;
I haven't the gift of the gab, my boys; so each
                        man to his gun;
If she's not mine in half an hour, I'll flog each
                        mother's son.
     For odds bobs, hammer and tongs, long as
                        I've been to sea,
      I've fought 'gainst every odds—and I've
                        gained the victory!"

We fought for twenty minutes, when the French-
                        man had enough;
"I little thought," said he, "that your men were
                        of such stuff":
Our captain took the Frenchman's sword, a low
                        bow made to he;
"I haven't the gift of the gab, monsieur, but
                        polite I wish to be.
     And odds bobs, hammer and tongs, long as
                        I've been to sea,
      I've fought 'gainst every odds—and I've
                        gained the victory!"

Our captain sent for all of us: "My merry men,"
                                        said he,
"I haven't the gift of the gab, my lads, but yet I
                                        thankful be:
You've done your duty handsomely, each man
                                        stood to his gun;
If you hadn't, you villains, as sure as day, I'd
                                have flogged each mother's son,
For odds bobs, hammer and tongs, as long
                                        as I'm at sea,
I'll fight 'gainst every odds—and I'll gain
                                        the victory!"

FREDERICK MARRYAT

The Spanish Armado

SOME years of late, in eighty-eight,
    As I do well remember,
It was, some say, the middle of May,
    And some say in September,
        And some say in September.

The Spanish train launched forth amain,
    With many a fine bravado,
Their (as they thought, but it proved not)
    Invincible Armado,
        Invincible Armado.

114

There was a man that dwelt in Spain,
   Who shot well with a gun a,
Don Pedro hight, as black a wight
   As the Knight of the Sun a,
      As the Knight of the Sun a.

King Philip made him Admiral,
   And bade him not to stay a,
But to destroy both man and boy
   And so to come away a,
      And so to come away a.

Their navy was well-victuallèd
   With bisket, pease, and bacon,
They brought two ships, well fraught with
   But I think they were mistaken,   [whips
      But I think they were mistaken.

Their men were young, munition strong,
   And to do us more harm a,
They thought it meet to join their fleet
   All with the Prince of Parma,
      All with the Prince of Parma.

They coasted round about our land,
   And so came in by Dover:
But we had men set on 'em then,
   And threw the rascals over,
      And threw the rascals over.

The Queen was then at Tilbury,
  What could we more desire a?
Sir Francis Drake for her sweet sake
  Did set them all on fire a,
    Did set them all on fire a.

Then straight they fled by sea and land,
  That one man killed threescore a,
And had not they all run away,
  In truth he had killed more a,
    In truth he had killed more a.

Then let them neither bray nor boast,
  But if they come again a,
Let them take heed they do not speed
  As they did you know when a,
    As they did you know when a.

ANONYMOUS

ADVENTURES

The Silver Penny

"SAILORMAN, I'll give to you
   My bright silver penny,
If out to sea you'll sail me
   And my dear sister Jenny."

"Get in, young sir, I'll sail ye
   And your dear sister Jenny,
But pay she shall her golden locks
   Instead of your penny."

They sail away, they sail away,
   O fierce the winds blew!
The foam flew in clouds
   And dark the night grew!

And all the green sea-water
   Climbed steep into the boat;
Back to the shore again
   Sail they will not.

Drowned is the sailorman,
   Drowned is sweet Jenny,
And drowned in the deep sea
   A bright silver penny.

WALTER DE LA MARE

A Ship Sails up to Bideford

A SHIP sails to Bideford
　　Upon a western breeze,
Mast by mast, sail over sail,
She rises from the seas,
And sights the hills of Devon
And the misty English trees.

She comes from Eastern islands;
The sun is in her hold;
She bears the fruit of Jaffa,
Dates, oranges, and gold;

She brings the silk of China,
And bales of Persian dyes,
And birds with sparkling feathers,
And snakes with diamond eyes.

She's gliding in the sunlight
As white as any gull;
The East is gliding with her
The shadows of her hull.

A ship sails up to Bideford
Upon a western breeze,
With fruits of eastern summers
She rises from the seas,
And sights the hills of Devon
And the misty English trees.

HERBERT ASQUITH

118

Eldorado

Gaily bedight,
   A gallant Knight,
In sunshine and in shadow
   Had journeyed long,
   Singing a song,
In search of Eldorado.

But he grew old—
   This Knight so bold,—
And o'er his heart a shadow
   Fell as he found
   No spot of ground
That looked like Eldorado.

And, as his strength
   Failed him at length,
He met a pilgrim shadow—
   "Shadow," said he,
   "Where can it be—
This land of Eldorado?"

"Over the Mountains
   Of the Moon,
Through the Valley of the Shadow
   Ride, boldly ride,"
   The shade replied,—
"If you seek for Eldorado!"

EDGAR ALLAN POE

Tartary

IF I were Lord of Tartary,
    Myself and me alone,
My bed should be of ivory,
    Of beaten gold my throne;
And in my court should peacocks flaunt,
And in my forest tigers haunt,
And in my pools great fishes slant
    Their fins athwart the sun.

If I were Lord of Tartary,
    Trumpeters every day
To every meal should summon me,
    And in my courtyard bray;
And in the evening lamps would shine
Yellow as honey, red as wine,
While harp, and flute, and mandoline,
    Made music sweet and gay.

If I were Lord of Tartary,
    I'd wear a robe of beads,
White, and gold, and green they'd be—
    And clustered thick as seeds;
And ere should wane the morning-star,
I'd don my robe and scimitar,
And zebras seven should draw my car
    Through Tartary's dark glades.

Lord of the fruits of Tartary,
    Her rivers silver-pale!
Lord of the hills of Tartary,
    Glen, thicket, wood, and dale!
Her flashing stars, her scented breeze,
Her trembling lakes, like foamless seas,
Her bird-delighting citron-trees
    In every purple vale!

WALTER DE LA MARE

There Was a Knicht

THERE was a knicht riding frae the east,
    Jennifer gentle an' rosemaree.
Who had been wooing at monie a place,
    As the doo[1] flies owre the mulberry tree.

He cam' unto a widow's door,
And speird whare her three dochters were.

"The auldest ane's to a washing gane,
The second's to a baking gane.

"The youngest ane's to a wedding gane,
And it will be nicht or she be hame."

He sat him doun upon a stane,
Till thir three lasses cam' tripping hame.

[1] doo: dove.

121

The auldest ane she let him in,
And pinned the door wi' a siller pin.

The second ane she made his bed,
And laid saft pillows unto his head.

The youngest ane was bauld and bricht,
And she tarried for words wi' this unco
                                    knicht:—

"Gin ye will answer me questions ten,
The morn ye sall me make your ain:—

"O what is higher nor the tree?
And what is deeper nor the sea?

"Or what is heavier nor the lead?
And what is better nor the bread?

"Or what is whiter nor the milk?
Or what is safter nor the silk?

"Or what is sharper nor a thorn?
Or what is louder nor a horn?

"Or what is greener nor the grass?
Or what is waur nor a woman was?"

"O heaven is higher nor the tree,
And hell is deeper nor the sea.

"O sin is heavier nor the lead,
The blessings better nor the bread.

"The snaw is whiter nor the milk,
And the down is safter nor the silk.

"Hunger is sharper nor a thorn,
And shame is louder nor a horn.

"The pies are greener nor the grass,
And Clootie's[1] waur nor a woman was."

As sune as she the fiend did name,
    Jennifer gentle an' rosemaree,
He flew awa' in a blazing flame,
    As the doo flies owre the mulberry tree.

ANONYMOUS

[1] *Clootie* was a name for the Devil. *Cloot* is a Scots word for a hoof.

Singing Leaves

"WHAT fairings will ye that I bring?"
    Said the King to his daughters three;
"For I to Vanity Fair am bound,
    Now say what shall they be?"

Then up and spake the eldest daughter,
    That lady tall and grand:
"Oh, bring me pearls and diamonds great,
    And gold rings for my hand."

Thereafter spake the second daughter,
    That was both white and red;
"For me bring silks that will stand alone,
    And a gold comb for my head."

Then came the turn of the least daughter,
    That was whiter than thistle-down,
And among the gold of her blithesome hair
    Dim shone the golden crown.

"There came a bird this morning,
    And sang 'neath my bower eaves,
Till I dreamed, as his music made me,
    'Ask thou for the Singing Leaves.'"

Then the brow of the King swelled crimson
    With a flush of angry scorn:
"Well have ye spoken, my two eldest,
    And chosen as ye were born;

"But she, like a thing of peasant race,
    That is happy binding the sheaves";
Then he saw her dead mother in her face,
    And said, "Thou shalt have thy leaves."

He mounted and rode three days and nights,
    Till he came to Vanity Fair,
And 'twas easy to buy the gems and the silk,
    But no Singing Leaves were there.

Then deep in the greenwood rode he,
    And asked of every tree,
"Oh, if you have a Singing Leaf,
    I pray you give it me!"

But the trees all kept their counsel,
    And never a word said they,
Only there sighed from the pine-tops
    A music of seas far away.

Only the pattering aspen
    Made a sound of growing rain,
That fell ever faster and faster,
    Then faltered to silence again.

"Oh, where shall I find a little foot-page
    That would win both hose and shoon,
And will bring to me the Singing Leaves,
    If they grow under the moon?"

Then lightly turned him Walter the page,
   By the stirrup as he ran:
"Now pledge you me the truesome word
   Of a King and a gentleman,

"That you will give me the first, first thing
   You meet at your castle-gate,
And the Princess shall get the Singing Leaves,
   Or mine be a traitor's fate."

The King's head dropped upon his breast
   A moment as it might be;
"'Twill be my dog," he thought, and said,
   "My faith I plight to thee."

Then Walter took from next his heart
   A packet small and thin,
"Now give you this to the Princess Anne,
   The Singing Leaves are therein."

As the King rode in at his castle-gate
   A maiden to meet him ran,
And "Welcome, father!" she laughed and cried
   Together, the Princess Anne.

"Lo, here the Singing Leaves," quoth he,
   "And woe, but they cost me dear!"
She took the packet, and the smile
   Deepened down beneath the tear.

It deepened down till it reached her heart,
    And then gushed up again,
And lighted her tears as the sudden sun
    Transfigures the summer rain.

And the first Leaf, when it was opened,
    Sang: "I am Walter the page,
And the songs I sing 'neath thy window
    Are my only heritage."

And the second Leaf sang: "But in the land
    That is neither on earth nor sea,
My lute and I are lords of more
    Than thrice this kingdom's fee."

And the third Leaf sang, "Be mine! Be mine!"
    And ever it sang "Be mine!"
Then sweeter it sang, and ever sweeter,
    And said, "I am thine, thine, thine!"

At the first Leaf she grew pale enough,
    At the second she turned aside,
At the third 'twas as if a lily flushed
    With a rose's red heart's tide.

"Good counsel gave the bird," said she,
    "I have my hope thrice o'er,
For they sing to my very heart," she said,
    "And it sings to them ever more."

She brought to him her beauty and truth,
　　Birth and broad earldoms three,
And he made her Queen of the broader lands
　　He held of his lute in fee.

JAMES RUSSELL LOWELL

The Wee Wee Man

As I was walking all alone
　　Between a water and a wa',
And there I spied a wee wee man,
　　And he was the least that e'er I saw.

His legs were scarce a shathmont's[1] length,
　　And thick and thimber[2] was his thigh;
Between his brows there was a span,
　　And between his shoulders there was three.

He took up a mickle stone,
　　And he flung it as far as I could see;
Though I had been a Wallace wight,
　　I couldn't have lifted it to my knee.

[1] A distance of about six inches. *Shath* seems to be connected with a Breton word meaning *a span*.
[2] Strong.

"O wee wee man, but thou art strong!
    O tell me where thy dwelling be."
"My dwelling's down at yon bonny bower;
    O will you go with me and see?"

On we leapt, and away we rode,
    Till we came to yon bonny green;
We lighted down for to bait[1] our horse,
    And out there came a lady fine.

Four and twenty at her back,
    And they were all clad out in green;
Though the King of Scotland had been there,
    The worst o' them might ha' been his queen.

On we leapt, and away we rode,
    Till we came to yon bonny hall,
Where the roof was o' the beaten gold
    And the floor was o' the crystal all.

When we came to the stair-foot,
    Ladies were dancing jimp[2] and sma',
—But in the twinkling of an eye
    My wee wee man was clean awa'.

ANONYMOUS

[1] Refresh.   [2] Slim.

Earl Haldan's Daughter

IT was Earl Haldan's daughter,
　　She looked across the sea;
She looked across the water;
　　And long and loud laughed she:
"The locks of six princesses
　　Must be my marriage fee,
So hey bonny boat, and ho bonny boat!
　　Who comes a-wooing me?"

It was Earl Haldan's daughter,
　　She walked along the sand;
When she was aware of a knight so fair,
　　Come sailing to the land.
His sails were all of velvet,
　　His mast of beaten gold,
And "Hey bonny boat, and ho bonny boat!
　　Who saileth here so bold?"

"The locks of five princesses
　　I won beyond the sea;
I clipt their golden tresses,
　　To fringe a cloak for thee.
One handful yet is wanting,
　　But one of all the tale;[1]
So hey bonny boat, and ho bonny boat!
　　Furl up thy velvet sail!"

[1] Number.

He leapt into the water,
　　That rover young and bold,
He gript Earl Haldan's daughter,
　　He clipt her locks of gold:
"Go weep, go weep, proud maiden,
　　The tale is full to-day.
Now hey bonny boat, and ho bonny boat!
　　Sail Westward ho! away!"

CHARLES KINGSLEY

The Spanish Main

I've asked a great many people,
　　But nobody seems to know
How the pirates kept their Christmas
　　In the days of long ago.

How many loaded galleons
　　On Christmas Day they sank,
And how many merchant seamen
　　They made to walk the plank.

Or whether they chanted carols
　　As round the decks they rolled,
And made each other presents
　　Out of their hoards of gold;

131

And covered a mast with green leaves
And called it a Christmas-tree,
And hung it with shining sequins[1]
On the shore of a tropical sea.

And lit the rum round the pudding
And cursed in a kindly way,
But refused to do any business
Because it was Christmas Day.

I've asked a great many people,
But nobody seems to know,
How the pirates kept their Christmas
In the days of long ago.

E. V. KNOX

[1] An ancient gold coin of Venice.

The Wraggle Taggle Gipsies

THERE were three gipsies a-come to my door,
And downstairs ran this a-lady, O!
One sang high, and another sang low,
And the other sang, Bonny, bonny Biscay, O!

Then she pulled off her silk-finished gown
And put on hose of leather, O!
The ragged, ragged rags about our door—
She's gone with the wraggle taggle gipsies, O!

It was late last night, when my lord came home,
Enquiring for his a-lady, O!
The servants said, on every hand:
"She's gone with the wraggle taggle gipsies, O!"

"O saddle to me my milk-white steed.
Go and fetch me my pony, O!
That I may ride and seek my bride,
Who is gone with the wraggle taggle gipsies, O!"

O he rode high and he rode low,
He rode through woods and copses too,
Until he came to an open field,
And there he espied his a-lady, O!

"What makes you leave your house and land?
What makes you leave your money, O?
What makes you leave your new-wedded lord;
To go with the wraggle taggle gipsies, O?"

"What care I for my house and my land?
What care I for my money, O?
What care I for my new-wedded lord?
I'm off with the wraggle taggle gipsies, O!"

"Last night you slept on a goose-feather bed,
With the sheet turned down so bravely, O!
And to-night you'll sleep in a cold open field,
Along with the wraggle taggle gipsies, O!"

"What care I for a goose-feather bed,
With the sheet turned down so bravely, O?
For to-night I shall sleep in a cold open field,
Along the with wraggle taggle gipsies, O!"

ANONYMOUS

Boot and Saddle

Boot, saddle, to horse, and away!
   Rescue my Castle, before the hot day
Brightens to blue from its silvery grey,
   Boot, saddle, to horse, and away!

Ride past the suburbs, asleep as you'd say;
Many's the friend there, will listen and pray
"God's luck to gallants that strike up the lay—
   Boot, saddle, to horse and away."

Forty miles off, like a roebuck at bay,
Flouts Castle Brancepeth the Roundheads' array:
Who laughs, "Good fellows, ere this, by my fay,
   Boot, saddle, to horse, and away?"

Who? My wife Gertrude; that, honest and gay,
Laughs when you talk of surrendering, "Nay!
I've better counsellors; what counsel they?
   Boot, saddle, to horse, and away!"

ROBERT BROWNING

134

Kingdoms

THE sailor tells the children
    His stories of the sea,
Their eyes look over the water
    To where his wonders be:

The flowers as big as tea-cups,
    The great big butterflies
The long unfooted beaches
    Where stored-up treasure lies.

More than a thousand islands
    Each curved around its pool:
All Kingdoms filled with sunlight,
    Where no one goes to school;

The fish that leave the water
    In sudden beads of light
The birds as blue as china;
    The flies that gleam by night . . .

Till, slowly, I remember
    A wistful place; and then,—
The story of that Kingdom
    First told to longshoremen.

OLIVER ST. JOHN GOGARTY

Hervé Riel

ON the sea and at the Hogue, sixteen hundred
                              ninety-two,
  Did the English fight the French,—woe to
                               France!
And, the thirty-first of May, helter-skelter through
                              the blue,
  Like a crowd of frightened porpoises a shoal of
                           sharks pursue,
    Came crowding ship on ship to Saint-Malo on
                         the Rance,
With the English fleet in view.

'Twas the squadron that escaped, with the victor in
                           full chase;
  First and foremost of the drove, in his great
                        ship, Damfreville;
    Close on him fled, great and small,
    Twenty-two good ships in all;
And they signalled to the place
"Help the winners of a race!
  Get us guidance, give us harbour, take us quick
                     —or, quicker still,
  Here's the English can and will!"

Then the pilots of the place put out brisk and
                            leapt on board;
  "Why, what hope or chance have ships like
                        these to pass?" laughed they:
"Rocks to starboard, rocks to port, all the passage
                            scarred and scored—
Shall the *Formidable* here, with her twelve and
                            eighty guns,
  Think to make the river-mouth by the single
                            narrow way,
Trust to enter—where 'tis ticklish for a craft of
                            twenty tons,
      And with flow at full beside?
      Now, 'tis slackest ebb of tide.
      Reach the mooring? Rather say,
While rock stands or water runs,
      Not a ship will leave the bay!"

Then was called a council straight.
Brief and bitter the debate:
"Here's the English at our heels; would you have
                        them take in tow
All that's left us of the fleet, linked together
                        stern and bow,
For a prize to Plymouth Sound?
Better run the ships aground!"
    (Ended Damfreville his speech).
"Not a minute more to wait!
    Let the Captains all and each
    Shove ashore, then blow up, burn the vessels on
                            the beach!
France must undergo her fate.

"Give the word!" But no such word
Was ever spoke or heard;
   For up stood, for out stepped, for in struck amid
                          all these—
A Captain? A Lieutenant? A Mate—first, second,
                          third?
      No such man of mark, and meet
      With his betters to compete!
But a simple Breton sailor pressed by Tourville
                     for the fleet,
A poor coasting-pilot he, Hervé Riel the Croisickese.

And, "What mockery or malice have we here?"
                     cries Hervé Riel:
  "Are you mad, you Malouins? Are you cowards,
                  fools, or rogues?
Talk to me of rocks and shoals, me who took the
                  soundings, tell
On my fingers every bank, every shallow, every
                      swell
  'Twixt the offing here and Greve where the
               river disembogues?[1]
Are you bought by English gold? Is it love the
                 lying's for?
      Morn and eve, night and day,
      Have I piloted your bay,
Entered free and anchored fast at the foot of Solidor.
Burn the fleet and ruin France? That were
              worse than fifty Hogues!
   Sirs, they know I speak the truth! Sirs,
             believe me there's a way!

[1] Falls into the sea.

Only let me lead the line,
   Have the biggest ship to steer,
   Get this *Formidable* clear,
Make the others follow mine,
And I lead them, most and least, by a passage I
                                    know well,
      Right to Solidor past Grève,
         And there lay them safe and sound;
      And if one ship misbehave,—
         Keel so much as grate the ground—
Why, I've nothing but my life,—here's my head!"
                              cries Hervé Riel.

Not a minute more to wait.
"Steer us in, then, small and great!
   Take the helm, lead the line, save the
                        squadron!" cried its chief.
Captains, give the sailor place!
   He is Admiral, in brief.
Still the north wind, by God's grace!
See the noble fellow's face,
As the big ship, with a bound,
Clears the entry like a hound,
Keeps the passage, as its inch of way were the
                              wide sea's profound!
      See, safe thro' shoal and rock,
      How they follow in a flock,
Not a ship that misbehaves, not a keel that grates
                              the ground,

Not a spar that comes to grief!
The peril, see, is past,
All are harboured to the last,
And just as Hervé Riel hollas "Anchor!"—sure
                                        as fate,

Up the English come—too late!

So, the storm subsides to calm:
    They see the green trees wave
    On the heights o'erlooking Grève.
Hearts that bled are stanch'd with balm,
"Just our rapture to enhance,
    Let the English rake the bay,
Gnash their teeth and glare askance
    As they cannonade away!
'Neath rampired Solidor pleasant riding on the
                                        Rance!"

How hope succeeds despair on each Captain's
                                        countenance!

Out burst all with one accord,
        "This is Paradise for Hell!
    Let France, let France's King
    Thank the man that did the thing!"
What a shout, and all one word,
        "Hervé Riel!"
As he stepped in front once more.
    Not a symptom of surprise
    In the frank blue Breton eyes.
Just the same man as before.

Then said Damfreville, "My friend,
I must speak out at the end,
　　Though I find the speaking hard.
Praise is deeper than the lips:
You have saved the King his ships,
　　You must name your own reward.
'Faith, our sun was near eclipse!
Demand whate'er you will,
France remains your debtor still.
Ask to heart's content and have! or my name's
　　　　　　　　　　　　not Damfreville."

Then a beam of fun outbroke
On the bearded mouth that spoke,
As the honest heart laughed through
Those frank eyes of Breton blue:
"Since I needs must say my say,
　　Since on board the duty's done,
　　And from Malo Roads to Croisic Point, what is
　　　　　　　　　　　　it but a run?—
Since 'tis ask and have, I may—
　　Since the others go ashore—
Come! A good whole holiday!
　　Leave to go and see my wife, whom I call the
　　　　　　　　　　　　Belle Aurore!"
That he asked, and that he got—nothing more.

Name and deed alike are lost:
Not a pillar nor a post
  In his Croisic keeps alive the feat as it befell;
Not a head in white and black
On a single fishing smack,
In memory of the man but for whom had gone to
                              wrack

  All that France saved from the fight whence
                  England bore the bell.

Go to Paris, rank on rank
  Search the heroes flung pell-mell
On the Louvre, face and flank!
  You shall look long enough ere you come to
                    Hervé Riel.

So for better and for worse,
Hervé Riel, accept my verse!
In my verse, Hervé Riel, do thou once more
Save the squadron, honour France, love thy wife,
                the Belle Aurore.

ROBERT BROWNING

The Jackdaw of Rheims

THE Jackdaw sat on the Cardinal's chair!
 Bishop and abbot and prior were there;
 Many a monk, and many a friar,
 Many a knight, and many a squire,
With a great many more of lesser degree—
In sooth a goodly company;
And they served the Lord Primate on bended knee.
 Never, I ween, was a prouder seen,
Read of in books, or dreamt of in dreams,
Than the Cardinal Lord Archbishop of Rheims!

 In and out, through the motley rout,
That little Jackdaw kept hopping about;
 Here and there, like a dog in a fair,
 Over comfits and cakes, and dishes and plates,
Cowl and cope, and rochet and pall,
Mitre and crosier—he hopp'd upon all!
 With saucy air, he perch'd on the chair

Where, in state, the great Lord Cardinal sat
In the great Lord Cardinal's great red hat;
  And he peer'd in the face of his Lordship's
                              Grace,
With a satisfied look, as if he would say,
"We two are the greatest folks here to-day!"
  And the priests, with awe, as such freaks
                             they saw,
Said, "The Devil must be in that little Jackdaw!"

The feast was over, the board was clear'd,
The flawns[1] and the custards had all disappear'd,
And six little singing boys—dear little souls—
In nice clean faces, and nice white stoles,
  Came, in order due, two by two,
Marching that grand refectory through.
A nice little boy held a golden ewer,
Emboss'd and fill'd with water, as pure
As any that flows between Rheims and Namur,
Which a nice little boy stood ready to catch
In a fine golden hand-basin made to match.
Two nice little boys, rather more grown,
Carried lavender-water and eau-de-Cologne;
And a nice little boy had a nice cake of soap,
Worthy of washing the hands of the Pope.
  One little boy more a napkin bore,
Of the best white diaper, fringed with pink,
And a Cardinal's hat mark'd in "permanent ink."

[1] Cheese cakes.

The great Lord Cardinal turns at the sight
Of these nice little boys dress'd all in white:
    From his finger he draws his costly turquoise;
And, not thinking at all about little Jackdaws,
    Deposits it straight by the side of his plate,
While the nice little boys on his Eminence wait;
Till, when nobody's dreaming of any such thing,
That little Jackdaw hops off with the ring!

There's a cry and a shout, and a deuce of a rout,
And nobody seems to know what they're about,
But the monks have their pockets turn'd inside out;
    The friars are kneeling, and hunting, and feeling
The carpet, the floor, and the walls, and the
                        ceiling.
    The Cardinal drew off each plum-colour'd shoe,
And left his red stockings exposed to the view;
    He peeps, and he feels in the toes and the heels;
They turn up the dishes,—they turn up the
                      plates,—
They take up the poker and poke out the grates,
    —They turn up the rugs, they examine the
                    mugs:—
    But no!—no such thing;—they can't find THE
                    RING!
And the abbot declared that, "when nobody twigg'd
                    it,
Some rascal or other had popp'd in,
            and prigg'd it!"

The Cardinal rose with a dignified look,
He call'd for his candle, his bell, and his book!
  And in holy anger, and pious grief,
  He solemnly cursed that rascally thief!
  He cursed him at board, he cursed him in bed;
  From the sole of his foot to the crown of his
                                     head;
  He cursed him in sleeping, that every night
  He should dream of the devil, and wake in a
                                     fright;
  He cursed him in eating, he cursed him in
                                 drinking,
  He cursed him in coughing, in sneezing, in
                                 winking;
  He cursed him in sitting, in standing, in lying;
  He cursed him in walking, in riding, in flying,
  He cursed him in living, he cursed him in
                                  dying!—
Never was heard such a terrible curse!
  But what gave rise to no little surprise,
Nobody seem'd one penny the worse!

  The day was gone, the night came on,
The monks and the friars, they search'd till dawn:
  When the sacristan saw, on crumpled claw,
Come limping a poor little lame Jackdaw!
  No longer gay, as on yesterday;
His feathers all seem'd to be turn'd the wrong
                                    way;

His pinions droop'd—he could hardly stand,—
His head was as bald as the palm of your hand;
    His eyes so dim, so wasted each limb,
That, heedless of grammar, they all cried, "THAT'S
                                                HIM!—
That's the scamp that has done this scandalous
                                            thing!
That's the thief that has got my Lord Cardinal's
                                            Ring!"

    The poor little Jackdaw, when the monks he saw,
Feebly gave vent to a ghost of a caw;
And turn'd his bald head, as much as to say,
"Pray, be so good as to walk this way!"
    Slower and slower he limp'd on before,
Till they came to the back of the belfry door,
    Where the first thing they saw, midst the sticks
                                            and the straw,
Was the RING in the nest of that little Jackdaw!

Then the great Lord Cardinal call'd for his book,
And off that terrible curse he took;
    The mute expression served in lieu of confession,
    And being thus coupled with full restitution,
    The Jackdaw got plenary absolution!
    —When those words were heard, that poor little
                                                bird
Was so changed in a moment, 'twas really absurd.
    He grew sleek, and fat; in addition to that,
A fresh crop of feathers came thick as a mat!

His tail waggled more even than before;
But no longer it wagg'd with an impudent air,
No longer he perch'd on the Cardinal's chair.

He hopp'd now about with a gait devout;
At Matins, at Vespers, he never was out;
And, so far from any more pilfering deeds,
He always seem'd telling the Confessor's beads.
If any one lied—or if any one swore—
Or slumber'd in prayer-time and happen'd to snore,

That good Jackdaw would give a great "Caw!"
As much as to say, "Don't do so any more!"
While many remark'd, as his manners they saw,
That they "never had known such a pious
                                    Jackdaw!"

He long lived the pride of that country-side,
And, at last, in the odour of sanctity died;
When, as words were too faint his merits to
                                    paint,
The Conclave determined to make him a Saint!
And on newly-made Saints and Popes, as you know,
It's the custom, at Rome, new names to bestow,
So they canonized him by the name of "JIM
                                    CROW."

"THOMAS INGOLDSBY"
R. H. BARHAM

148

Green Broom

THERE was an old man lived out in the wood,
  His trade was a-cutting of Broom, green
                                      Broom;
He had but one son without thrift, without good,
  Who lay in his bed till 'twas noon, bright noon.

The old man awoke, one morning and spoke,
  He swore he would fire the room, that room,
If his John would not rise and open his eyes,
  And away to the wood to cut Broom, green
                                        Broom.

So Johnny arose, and he slipped on his clothes,
  And away to the wood to cut Broom, green
                                        Broom,
He sharpened his knives, for once he contrives
  To cut a great bundle of Broom, green Broom.

When Johnny passed under a lady's fine house,
  Passed under a lady's fine room, fine room,
She called to her maid, "Go fetch me," she said,
  "Go fetch me the boy that sells Broom, green
                                        Broom."

When Johnny came in to the lady's fine house,
  And stood in the lady's fine room, fine room;
"Young Johnny," she said, "will you give up
                                your trade,
  And marry a lady in bloom, full bloom?"

Johnny gave his consent, and to church they both
went,
And he wedded the lady in bloom, full bloom.
At market and fair, all folks do declare,
There is none like the Boy that sold Broom,
green Broom.

ANONYMOUS

The Neckan

IN summer, on the headlands,
    The Baltic Sea along,
Sits Neckan with his harp of gold,
    And sings his plaintive song.

Green rolls beneath the headlands,
    Green rolls the Baltic Sea;
And there, below the Neckan's feet,
    His wife and children be.

He sings not of the ocean,
    Its shells and roses pale;
Of earth, of earth the Neckan sings,
    He hath no other tale.

He sits upon the headlands,
   And sings a mournful stave
Of all he saw and felt on earth
   Far from the kind sea-wave.

Sings how, a knight, he wander'd
   By castle, field, and town—
But earthly knights have harder hearts
   Than the sea-children own.

Sings of his earthly bridal—
   Priests, knights, and ladies gay.
"—And who art thou," the priest began,
   "Sir Knight, who wedd'st to-day?"—

"—I am no knight," he answer'd;
   "From the sea-waves I come."—
The knights drew sword, the ladies scream'd,
   The surpliced priest stood dumb.

He sings how from the chapel
   He vanish'd with his bride,
And bore her down to the sea-halls,
   Beneath the salt sea-tide.

He sings how she sits weeping
   'Mid shells that round her lie.
"False Neckan shares my bed," she weeps;
   "No Christian mate have I."

He sings how through the billows
    He rose to earth again,
And sought a priest to sign the cross,
    That Neckan Heaven might gain.

He sings how, on an evening,
    Beneath the birch-trees cool,
He sate and play'd his harp of gold;
    Beside the river-pool.

Beside the pool sate Neckan—
    Tears fill'd his mild blue eye.
On his white mule, across the bridge,
    A cassock'd priest rode by.

"—Why sitt'st thou there, O Neckan,
    And play'st thy harp of gold?
Sooner shall this my staff bear leaves,
    Than thou shalt Heaven behold."—

The cassock'd priest rode onwards,
And vanish'd with his mule;
And Neckan in the twilight grey
    Wept by the river-pool.

In summer, on the headlands,
    The Baltic Sea along,
Sits Neckan with his harp of gold,
    And sings this plaintive song.

MATTHEW ARNOLD

The Gipsy Laddie

IT was late in the night when the Squire
    came home
Enquiring for his lady.
His servant made a sure reply:
"She's gone with the gipsum Davy."
    Rattle tum a gipsum gipsum
    Rattle tum a gipsum Davy.

"O go catch up my milk-white steed,
The black one's not so speedy,
I'll ride all night till broad daylight,
Or overtake my lady."

He rode and he rode till he came to the town,
He rode till he came to Barley.
The tears came rolling down his cheeks,
And then he spied his lady.

"It's come go back, my dearest dear,
Come go back, my honey;
It's come go back, my dearest dear,
And you never shall lack for money."

"I won't go back, my dearest dear,
I won't go back, my honey;
For I wouldn't give a kiss from gipsum's lips
For you and all your money."

"It's go pull off those snow-white gloves,
A-made of Spanish leather,
And give to me your lily-white hand,
And bid farewell for ever."

It's she pulled off those snow-white gloves,
A-made of Spanish leather,
And gave to him her lily-white hand,
And bade farewell for ever.

She soon ran through her gay clothing,
Her velvet shoes and stockings;
Her gold ring off her finger's gone,
And the gold plate off her bosom.

"O once I had a house and land,
Feather-bed and money;
But now I've come to an old straw pad
With the gipsies dancing round me."

ANONYMOUS

154

The Pied Piper of Hamelin

I

Hamelin Town's in Brunswick,
  By famous Hanover city;
The River Weser, deep and wide,
Washes its walls on the southern side;
A pleasanter spot you never spied;
  But, when begins my ditty,
Almost five hundred years ago,
To see the townsfolk suffer so
  From vermin, was a pity.

II

  Rats!
They fought the dogs and killed the cats,
  And bit the babies in the cradles,
And ate the cheeses out of the vats,
  And licked the soup from the cooks' own ladles,
Split open the kegs of salted sprats,
Made nests inside men's Sunday hats,
And even spoiled the women's chats
  By drowning their speaking
  With shrieking and squeaking
In fifty different sharps and flats.

III

At last the people in a body
  To the Town Hall came flocking:
"'Tis clear," cried they, "our Mayor's a noddy;
  And as for our Corporation—shocking
To think we buy gowns lined with ermine
For dolts that can't or won't determine
What's best to rid us of our vermin!
You hope, because you're old and obese,
To find in the furry civic robe ease?
Rouse up, Sirs! Give your brains a racking
To find the remedy we're lacking,
Or, sure as fate, we'll send you packing!"
At this the Mayor and Corporation
Quaked with a mighty consternation.

IV

An hour they sat in council;
  At length the Mayor broke silence:
"For a guilder I'd my ermine gown sell;
  I wish I were a mile hence!
It's easy to bid one rack one's brain—
I'm sure my poor head aches again,
I've scratched it so, and all in vain.
O for a trap, a trap, a trap!"
Just as he said this, what should hap
At the chamber door, but a gentle tap?
"Bless us!" cried the Mayor, "what's that?"
(With the Corporation as he sat,
Looking little though wondrous fat;

Nor brighter was his eye, nor moister
Than a too-long-opened oyster,
Save when at noon his paunch grew mutinous
For a plate of turtle, green and glutinous)
"Only a scraping of shoes on the mat?
Anything like the sound of a rat
Makes my heart go pit-a-pat!"

V

"Come in!"—the Mayor cried, looking bigger:
And in did come the strangest figure!
His queer long coat from heel to head
Was half of yellow and half of red,
And he himself was tall and thin,
With sharp blue eyes, each like a pin,
And light loose hair, yet swarthy skin,
No tuft on cheek nor beard on chin,
But lips where smiles went out and in;
There was no guessing his kith and kin:
And nobody could enough admire
The tall man and his quaint attire.
Quoth one: "It's as my great-grandsire,
Starting up at the Trump of Doom's tone,
Had walked this way from his painted tombstone!"

157

He advanced to the council-table:
And, "Please your honours," said he, "I'm able,
By means of a secret charm, to draw
All creatures living beneath the sun,
That creep or swim or fly or run,
After me so as you never saw!
And I chiefly use my charm
On creatures that do people harm,
The mole and toad and newt and viper;
And people call me the Pied Piper."
(And here they noticed round his neck
    A scarf of red and yellow stripe,
To match with his coat of the self-same check,
    And at the scarf's end hung a pipe;
And his fingers, they noticed, were ever straying
As if impatient to be playing
Upon his pipe, as low it dangled
Over his vesture so old-fangled.)
"Yet," said he, "poor piper as I am,
In Tartary I freed the Cham,
    Last June, from his huge swarms of gnats;
I eased in Asia the Nizam
    Of a monstrous brood of vampire-bats:
And as for what your brain bewilders,
    If I can rid your town of rats,
Will you give me a thousand guilders?"
"One? fifty thousand!"—was the exclamation
Of the astonished Mayor and Corporation.

Into the street the Piper stept,
  Smiling first a little smile,
As if he knew what magic slept
  In his quiet pipe the while;
Then, like a musical adept,
To blow the pipe his lips he wrinkled,
And green and blue his sharp eyes twinkled,
Like a candle-flame where salt is sprinkled;
And ere three shrill notes the pipe uttered,
You heard as if an army muttered;
And the muttering grew to a grumbling;
And the grumbling grew to a mighty rumbling;
And out of the houses the rats came tumbling.
Great rats, small rats, lean rats, brawny rats,
Brown rats, black rats, grey rats, tawny rats,
Grave old plodders, gay young friskers,
  Fathers, mothers, uncles, cousins,
Cocking tails and pricking whiskers.
  Families by tens and dozens,
Brothers, sisters, husbands, wives—
Followed the Piper for their lives.
From street to street he piped advancing,
And step for step they followed dancing,
Until they came to the River Weser,
  Wherein all plunged and perished!
—Save one who, stout as Julius Cæsar,
Swam across and lived to carry
  (As he, the manuscript he cherished)
To Rat-land home his commentary:

Which was, "At first shrill notes of the pipe,
I heard a sound as of scraping tripe,
And putting apples, wondrous ripe,
Into a cider-press's gripe:
And a moving away of pickle-tub-boards,
And a leaving ajar of conserve-cupboards,
And a drawing the corks of train-oil-flasks,
And a breaking the hoops of butter-casks:
And it seemed as if a voice
  (Sweeter far than by harp or by psaltery
Is breathed) called out, 'Oh, rats, rejoice!
  The world is grown to one vast drysaltery!
So munch on, crunch on, take your nuncheon,
Breakfast, supper, dinner, luncheon!'
And just as a bulky sugar-puncheon,
All ready staved, like a great sun shone
Glorious scarce an inch before me,
Just as methought it said, 'Come, bore me!'
—I found the Weser rolling o'er me."

VIII

You should have heard the Hamelin people
Ringing the bells till they rocked the steeple.
"Go," cried the Mayor, " and get long poles,
Poke out the nests, and block up the holes!
Consult with carpenters and builders,
And leave in our town not even a trace
Of the rats!"—when, suddenly, up the face
Of the Piper perked in the market-place,
With a "First, if you please, my thousand
                guilders!"

IX

A thousand guilders! The Mayor looked blue;
So did the Corporation too.
For council dinners made rare havoc
With Claret, Moselle, Vin-de-Grave, Hock;
And half the money would replenish
Their cellar's biggest butt with Rhenish.
To pay this sum to a wandering fellow
With a gipsy coat of red and yellow!
"Beside," quoth the Mayor, with a knowing wink,
"Our business was done at the river's brink;
We saw with our eyes the vermin sink,
And what's dead can't come to life, I think.
So, friend, we're not the folks to shrink
From the duty of giving you something for drink,
And a matter of money to put in your poke;
But as for the guilders, what we spoke
Of them, as you very well know, was in joke.
Beside, our losses have made us thrifty.
A thousand guilders! Come, take fifty!"

X

The Piper's face fell, and he cried
"No trifling! I can't wait, beside!
I've promised to visit by dinner-time
Bagdat, and accept the prime
Of the Head-Cook's pottage, all he's rich in,
For having left, in the Caliph's kitchen,
Of a nest of scorpions no survivor:
With him I proved no bargain-driver,

With you, don't think I'll bate a stiver!
And folks who put me in a passion
May find me pipe after another fashion."

XI

"How?" cried the Mayor, "d'ye think I brook
Being worse treated than a Cook?
Insulted by a lazy ribald
With idle pipe and vesture piebald?
You threaten us, fellow? Do your worst,
Blow your pipe until you burst!"

XII

Once more he stept into the street
　　And to his lips again
　　Laid his long pipe of smooth straight cane;
And ere he blew three notes (such sweet
Soft notes as yet a musician's cunning
　　Never gave the enraptured air)
There was a rustling that seemed like a bustling
Of merry crowds justling at pitching and hustling,
Small feet were pattering, wooden shoes clattering,
Little hands clapping and little tongues chattering,
And, like fowls in the farmyard when barley is
　　　　　　　　　　　　　　scattering,
Out came the children running.
All the little boys and girls,
With rosy cheeks and flaxen curls,
And sparkling eyes and teeth like pearls,
Tripping and skipping, ran merrily after
The wonderful music with shouting and laughter.

XIII

The Mayor was dumb, and the Council stood
As if they were changed into blocks of wood,
Unable to move a step, or cry
To the children merrily skipping by,
—Could only follow with the eye
That joyous crowd at the Piper's back.
But how the Mayor was on the rack,
And the wretched Council's bosoms beat,
As the Piper turned from the High Street
To where the Weser rolled its waters
Right in the way of their sons and daughters!
However, he turned from South to West,
And to Koppelberg Hill his steps addressed,
And after him the children pressed;
Great was the joy in every breast.
"He never can cross that mighty top!
He's forced to let the piping drop,
And we shall see our children stop!"
When, lo, as they reached the mountain-side,
A wondrous portal opened wide,
As if a cavern was suddenly hollowed;
And the Piper advanced and the children followed,
And when all were in to the very last,
The door in the mountain-side shut fast.
Did I say all? No! One was lame,
    And could not dance the whole of the way;
And in after years, if you would blame
    His sadness, he was used to say,—
"It's dull in our town since my playmates left!
I can't forget that I'm bereft

Of all the pleasant sights they see,
Which the Piper also promised me.
For he led us, he said, to a joyous land,
Joining the town and just at hand,
Where waters gushed and fruit-trees grew
And flowers put forth a fairer hue,
And everything was strange and new;
The sparrows were brighter than peacocks here,
And their dogs outran our fallow deer,
And honey-bees had lost their stings,
And horses were born with eagles' wings:
And just as I became assured
My lame foot would be speedily cured,
The music stopped and I stood still,
And found myself outside the hill,
Left alone against my will,
To go now limping as before,
And never hear of that country more!"

XIV

Alas, alas for Hamelin!
    There came into many a burgher's pate
    A text which says that heaven's gate
    Opes to the rich at as easy rate
As the needle's eye takes a camel in!
The Mayor sent East, West, North and South,
To offer the Piper, by word of mouth,
    Wherever it was men's lot to find him,
Silver and gold to his heart's content,
If he'd only return the way he went,
    And bring the children behind him.
But when they saw 'twas a lost endeavour,

And Piper and dancers were gone for ever,
They made a decree that lawyers never
    Should think their records dated duly
If, after the day of the month and the year
These words did not as well appear,
"And so long after what happened here
    On the Twenty-second of July,
Thirteen hundred and seventy-six";
And the better in memory to fix
The place of the children's last retreat,
They called it "The Pied Piper's Street"—
Where anyone playing on pipe or tabor
Was sure for the future to lose his labour.
Nor suffered they hostelry or tavern
    To shock with mirth a street so solemn;
But opposite the place of the cavern
    They wrote the story on a column,
And on the great church-window painted
The same, to make the world acquainted
How their children were stolen away,
And there it stands to this very day.
And I must not omit to say
That in Transylvania there's a tribe
Of alien people who ascribe
The outlandish ways and dress
On which their neighbours lay such stress,
To their fathers and mothers having risen
Out of some subterraneous prison
Into which they were trepanned
Long time ago in a mighty band
Out of Hamelin town in Brunswick land,
But how or why, they don't understand.

XV

So, Willy, let you and me be wipers
Of scores out with all men—especially pipers!
And, where they pipe us free from rats or from
mice,
If we've promised them aught, let us keep our
promise!

ROBERT BROWNING

Lord Ullin's Daughter

A CHIEFTAIN to the Highlands bound
Cries, "Boatman, do not tarry!
And I'll give thee a silver pound
To row us o'er the ferry!"

"Now who be ye would cross Lochgyle,
This dark and stormy water?"
"O, I'm the chief of Ulva's isle,
And this, Lord Ullin's daughter.

"And fast before her father's men
Three days we've fled together,
For should he find us in the glen,
My blood would stain the heather.

"His horsemen hard behind us ride—
Should they our steps discover
Then who will cheer my bonny bride
When they have slain her lover?"

Out spoke the hardy Highland wight,
   "I'll go, my chief, I'm ready:
It is not for your silver bright,
   But for your winsome lady:—

"And by my word! the bonny bird
   In danger shall not tarry;
So though the waves are raging white
   I'll row you o'er the ferry."

By this the storm grew loud apace,
   The water-wraith was shrieking;
And in the scowl of heaven each face
   Grew dark as they were speaking.

But still as wilder blew the wind,
   And as the night grew drearer,
Adown the glen rode armèd men,
   Their trampling sounded nearer.

"O haste thee, haste!" the lady cries,
   "Though tempests round us gather;
I'll meet the raging of the skies,
   But not an angry father."

The boat has left a stormy land,
   A stormy sea before her,—
When, O! too strong for human hand
   The tempest gathered o'er her.

And still they rowed amidst the roar
   Of waters fast prevailing:
Lord Ullin reached that fatal shore,—
   His wrath was changed to wailing.

For, sore dismayed, through storm and shade
   His child he did discover:—
One lovely hand she stretched for aid,
   And one was round her lover.

"Come back! come back!" he cried in grief,
   "Across this stormy water:
And I'll forgive your Highland chief,
   My daughter!—O my daughter!"

'Twas vain: the wild waves lashed the shore,
   Return or aid preventing:
The waters wild went o'er his child,
   And he was left lamenting.

THOMAS CAMPBELL

The Forsaken Merman

COME, dear children, let us away:
    Down and away below!
Now my brothers call from the bay;
    Now the great winds shorewards blow;
    Now the salt tides seawards flow;
Now the wild white horses play,
Champ and chafe and toss in the spray.
Children dear, let us away!
    This way, this way!

Call her once before you go.
    Call once yet.
In a voice that she will know:
    "Margaret! Margaret!"
Children's voices should be dear
(Call once more) to a mother's ear:
Children's voices, wild with pain—
Surely she will come again.
Call her once and come away;
    This way, this way!
"Mother dear, we cannot stay."
The wild white horses foam and fret.
    Margaret! Margaret!

Come, dear children, come away down!
    Call no more!
One last look at the white-walled town,
And the little grey church on the windy shore.
    Then come down.
She will not come though you call all day.
    Come away, come away!

Children dear, was it yesterday
We heard the sweet bells over the bay
In the caverns where we lay,
Through the surf and through the swell,
The far-off sound of a silver bell?
Sand-strewn caverns, cool and deep,
Where the winds are all asleep;
Where the spent lights quiver and gleam;
Where the salt weed sways in the stream;
Where the sea-beasts ranged all round
Feed in the ooze of their pasture-ground;
Where the sea-snakes coil and twine,
Dry their mail and bask in the brine;
Where great whales come sailing by,
Sail and sail, with unshut eye,
Round the world for ever and aye?
When did music come this way?
Children dear, was it yesterday?

Children dear, was it yesterday
(Call yet once) that she went away?
Once she sate with you and me,
On a red gold throne in the heart of the sea,
And the youngest sate on her knee.
She comb'd its bright hair, and she tended it well,
When down swung the sound of the far-off bell.
She sigh'd, she look'd up through the clear green

sea;

She said: "I must go, for my kinsfolk pray
In the little grey church on the shore to-day.

'Twill be Easter-time in the world—ah me!
And I lose my poor soul, Merman, here with
thee."
I said: "Go up, dear heart, through the waves!
Say thy prayer, and come back to the kind sea-
caves."
She smiled, she went up through the surf in the
bay.
Children dear, was it yesterday?

Children dear, were we long alone?
"The sea grows stormy, the little ones moan.
Long prayers," I said, "in the world they say.
Come!" I said, and we rose through the surf in
the bay.
We went up the beach, by the sandy down
Where the sea-stocks bloom, to the white-walled
town.
Through the narrow paved streets, where all was
still,
To the little grey church on the windy hill.
From the church came a murmur of folk at their
prayers,
But we stood without in the cold blowing airs.
We climbed on the graves, on the stones, worn
with rains,
And we gazed up the aisle through the small
leaded panes.
She sate by the pillar; we saw her clear:
"Margaret, hist! come quick, we are here.
Dear heart," I said, "we are long alone.

The sea grows stormy, the little ones moan."
But, ah, she gave me never a look,
For her eyes were sealed to the holy book!
Loud prays the priest; shut stands the door.
Come away, children, call no more!
Come away, come down, call no more!

Down, down, down!
Down to the depths of the sea!
She sits at her wheel in the humming town,
Singing most joyfully.
Hark, what she sings: "O joy, O joy,
For the humming street, and the child with its toy!
For the priest, and the bell, and the holy well—
For the wheel where I spun,
And the blessed light of the sun!"
And so she sings her fill,
Singing most joyfully,
Till the shuttle falls from her hand,
And the whizzing wheel stands still.
She steals to the window, and looks at the sand,
And over the sand at the sea;
And her eyes are set in a stare;
And anon there breaks a sigh,
And anon there drops a tear,
From a sorrow-clouded eye,
And a heart sorrow-laden,
A long, long sigh,
For the cold strange eyes of a little Mermaiden
And the gleam of her golden hair.

Come away, away, children!
  Come children, come down!
The hoarse wind blows colder;
  Lights shine in the town.
She will start from her slumber
  When gusts shake the door;
She will hear the winds howling,
  Will hear the waves roar.
We shall see, while above us
  The waves roar and whirl;
A ceiling of amber,
  A pavement of pearl.
Singing: "Here came a mortal,
  But faithless was she!
And alone dwell for ever
  The kings of the sea."

But, children, at midnight,
    When soft the winds blow,
When clear falls the moonlight,
    When spring-tides are low;
When sweet airs come seaward
    From heaths starred with broom,
And high rocks throw mildly
    On the blanched sands a gloom;
Up the still, glistening beaches,
    Up the creeks we will hie,
Over banks of bright seaweed
    The ebb-tide leaves dry,
We will gaze, from the sand-hills,
    At the white, sleeping town;
At the church on the hill-side—
    And then come back down.
Singing: "There dwells a loved one,
    But cruel is she!
She left lonely for ever
    The kings of the sea."

MATTHEW ARNOLD

Index of First Lines

	Page
A carrion crow sat on an oak	47
A chieftain to the Highlands bound	166
A furry coat has the bear to wear	8
A ship sails to Bideford	118
A song of enchantment I sang me there	71
A very old woman	60
A well there is in the west country	40
All but blind	1
Allen-a-dale has no fagot for burning	63
All winter through I bow my head	68
As beautiful Kitty one morning was tripping	48
As I was walking all alone	128
Beside a runnel build my shed	83
Boot, saddle, to horse, and away!	134
Clouds of children round the trough	66
Come, all you brave gallants, and listen a while	98
Come, dear children, let us away	169
Come follow, follow me	85
Come gentlemen all, and listen a while	94
Down came the horseman	58
From the bonnie bells of heather	108
From Oberon, in fairy land	88
Gaily bedight	119
Go fetch to me a pint o' wine	111
Godolphin Horne was nobly born	18
Hamelin Town's in Brunswick	155
Here comes the elephant	4
I come from haunts of coot and hern	69
If I were Lord of Tartary	120

	Page
I heard a bird at dawn	7
I'll sing you a good old song	50
I'll sing you a song, and a merry merry song	12
I'm a lean dog, a keen dog, a wild dog, and lone	2
In London once I lost my way	34
In summer on the headlands	150
In the cowslip pips I lie	13
I rise in the dawn and I kneel and blow	58
Isabel met an enormous bear	29
I sing of a maiden	49
It's a warm wind, the west wind, full of birds' cries	77
It was Earl Haldan's daughter	130
It was late in the night when the squire	153
I've asked a great many people	131
I wandered out one rainy day	11
Jellicle cats come out to-night	3
Lord Lundy from his earliest years	25
O Brignall banks are wild and fair	44
Old Meg she was a gipsy	62
One roads leads to London	73
On Friday morn as we set sail	55
On the sea and at the Hogue, sixteen hundred and ninety-two	136
O, to have a little house	59
Over hill, over dale	53
Piping down the valleys wild	43
Proud Maisie is in the wood	57
Said the shark to the flying-fish over the phone	20
Sailorman, I'll give to you	117
Saint Brandan sails the northern main	104
See you the dimpled track that runs	92
Some years of late, in eighty-eight	114
The auld wife sat at her ivied door	31
The bird in the corn	6
The captain stood on the carronade: "First lieutenant", says he	112
The cock is crowing	74

	Page
Their sails, as black as a starless night	107
The jackdaw sat on the cardinal's chair	143
The lion is the beast to fight	26
The night was creeping on the ground	72
The north wind sighed	76
The owl is abroad, the bat, and the toad	54
There lived a sage in the days of yore	24
There's no smoke in the chimney	85
There was a knicht riding frae the east	121
There was an old man lived out in the wood	149
There were three gipsies a-come to my door	132
There were three ravens sat on a tree	9
The Rum Tum Tugger is a curious cat	15
The sailor tells the children	135
The silver Severn water	82
The sun does arise	80
The sun was shining on the sea	36
The thistle down's flying, though the winds are all still	75
They went to sea in a sieve, they did	21
Waken, lords and ladies gay	52
Wearied arm and broken sword	65
"What fairings will ye that I bring?"	123
When first my brave Johnnie lad	103
When I play on my fiddle in Dooney	61
When I sailed out of Baltimore	17
Where the pools are bright and deep	79
"Will you walk a little faster?" said a whiting to a snail	27
"You are old, Father William," the young man said	33